# The London Underground
## Tube Stock

## J. GRAEME BRUCE OBE, BSc (Eng), FIEE, FIMech E, FCIT

IAN ALLAN
IN ASSOCIATION WITH THE

LONDON
IAN ALLAN LTD

# Contents

This book is a completely revised and updated version of a book first published in 1968 under the title *Tube Trains Under London*, which was about the development of Tube rolling stock built for 12ft diameter tunnels, so little mention is made of the Underground surface stock which conforms generally to a main line loading gauge. The book now takes the story beyond the development of the rolling stock for the Victoria Line to the 1986 Tube stock produced to point the way into the distant future of London's Underground.

Unless otherwise credited, all photographs which appear in this publication are from the London Transport Museum photographic library. Copy prints are not available from the publisher, but may be purchased on request from: London Transport Museum (Photographic Library), Covent Garden, London WC2E 7BB. Tel: 01-379 6344.

*Front cover, inset:*
**A colourful array of prototype 1987 Tube stock. From left to right: Metro-Cammell 'A' train, BREL 'B' train, Metro-Cammell 'C' train.** *LT*

*Front cover, main picture:*
**1959 Tube stock seen at Woodside Park on the Northern Line, High Barnet branch, in 1977.** *J. Glover*

*Title page:*
**A train of District Line 'D' stock climbs up into Barking on 26 July 1983 bound for Richmond.** *Kevin Lane*

First published 1988

ISBN 0 7110 1707 7

Published by Ian Allan Ltd, Shepperton, Surrey; and printed by Ian Allan Printing Ltd at their works at Coombelands in Runnymede, England

| | | |
|---|---|---|
| | Foreword to *Tube Trains Under London* | 3 |
| | Author's Note 1988 | 3 |
| | A Note of What Makes a Tube Train Go and Stop | 4 |
| 1. | The City & South London Railway | 7 |
| 2. | The Waterloo & City Railway | 17 |
| 3. | The Central London Railway | 25 |
| 4. | The Yerkes Tubes | 37 |
| 5. | Tube Extensions – Bakerloo 1914/22 | 45 |
| 6. | The First Air Door Stock 1919/22 | 49 |
| 7. | The First of the Standard Stock 1923/25 | 53 |
| 8. | More Standard Stock 1926/27 | 59 |
| 9. | Standard Stock Again 1929/30 | 63 |
| 10. | The Last of the Standard Stock | 67 |
| 11. | Pre-1938 Tube Stock | 71 |
| 12. | The Experimental Streamlined Stock 1935 | 73 |
| 13. | 1938 Tube Stock | 77 |
| 14. | The Nine-Car Train Experiment | 83 |
| 15. | 1949 Tube Stock | 85 |
| 16. | 1956/59 Tube Stock | 87 |
| 17. | 1962 Tube Stock | 91 |
| 18. | 1960 Tube Stock | 93 |
| 19. | 1967 Tube Stock | 99 |
| 20. | 1972 Tube Stock | 107 |
| 21. | 1973 Tube Stock | 113 |
| 22. | 1983 Tube Stock | 119 |
| 23. | 1986 Tube Stock | 123 |
| | Appendix | 126 |

# Foreword to *Tube Trains Under London*

by A. W. Manser BSc, FIMechE, FIEE, MILocoE, FRSA, CEng, formerly Chief Mechanical Engineer (Railways), London Transport

Too often in referring to the London Underground System the word 'tube' is applied quite indiscriminately. The tubes are, in fact, the bored circular tunnels, not to be confused with the 'cut and cover' tunnels of the District and Metropolitan Lines. These latter have their counterparts today in a great many other cities throughout the world. Nowhere else, however, is there to be found such an extensive system of bored tunnels as exists in London. In other places their use is largely confined to passage under waterways, whereas in London the whole system of deep level lines is constructed in this form.

The story of the London tubes may be said to have commenced with the construction of the Tower Hill subway, from Tower Hill on the north bank of the river to a corresponding point on the south bank, this subway being intended originally as a passenger subway through which conveyance was by means of small cable-hauled cars. This subway completed in 1870 was the first shield-driven cast-iron lined tunnel to be constructed anywhere in the world. P. W. Barlow, who was the Engineer-in-Charge, had served with the Brunels (Marc Isambard and Isambard Kingdom) on the construction of the Thames tunnel between Rotherhithe and Wapping — 1825 to 1843. He had evidently been impressed with the shield principle, even under the conditions of disastrous disadvantage which obtained on this earlier project and he conceived the idea of the circular tunnel with cast-iron lining.

This type of lining could, of course, be erected much more rapidly than brick lining, without any delay being occasioned by the need to allow the cement to harden. Mr Barlow seems also to have appreciated, perhaps by virtue of his experiences on the Thames tunnel work, the great desirability of keeping the tunnel down in the London clay and out of the alluvial strata nearer to the river bed. The existence of this stratum of moderate depth of so-called blue clay, which is ideal as a medium through which to tunnel, was no doubt responsible in no small measure for the rapid extension of the tube system after the success of the earlier line. Barlow's tunnel at Tower Hill was a mere 7ft in diameter and this was too small to be of effective use for railway purposes. The 'railway' with its cable haulage never seems to have operated satisfactorily and after less than a year's usage it was converted to a foot subway and later to a means of conveying hydraulic mains across the river.

The City & South London Railway, originally known as the City of London & Southwark Subway, which was not only the first tube railway to operate effectively but was the first complete electric railway in the world; that is, complete in the sense that it had stations, a proper form of signalling and rolling stock hauled by electric locomotives; it had a tunnel diameter of 10ft 2in. This still proved unreasonably restrictive in the design of the rolling stock and, subsequently, tunnels have been bored at larger diameters, those for the Victoria Line just over 12ft in diameter. There have been many who, over the years, have advocated the building of tunnels large enough to take stock of main line gauge but whenever the facts have been re-examined the

same conclusion has always been reached, that as value for money, in terms of passenger capacity against capital cost, the tube of the order of 12ft in diameter is the most attractive proposition for the London conditions. The tube train is a very effective quart in a pint pot — an eight-car train of the latest type being capable of carrying no less than 1,448 passengers. Admittedly, of this number only 304 will be seated but the vital function of the tube railways in London is to cater for the movement of the great mass of people at the peak hours and this can only be done by accepting that passengers with short or medium-short journeys cannot expect to rely on a seat when they are travelling at the peak hours.

In what follows, Mr Bruce tells the story of the rolling stock used on the tube lines right through from the City & South London Railway, at its inception, to the new rolling stock now in use for the Heathrow Extension, as well as details of London Transport's work on the new Fleet Line. It is an interesting history of technical progress and of the continuing endeavour to provide more capacity, more speed and more comfort, always within the confines of the 12ft diameter circle (and in most places even a little less).

Of the personalities involved, space in this foreword prohibits more than a brief reference, but to those who were fortunate enough to have known them, the names of W. A. Agnew and W. S. Graff-Baker, who together cover a span from 1907 to 1952, come immediately to mind. These men, by their care and perseverance, did much to develop the design of the London tube rolling stock and in this contributed greatly to the comfort of the London traveller.

*A. W. Manser*

---

# Author's Note 1988

At the time of the first edition in 1968 the rolling stock delivered for the Victoria Line was the ultimate in tube stock development. A revised and enlarged edition was produced in 1977, 10 years on, by which time further new rolling stock had begun running in the tube tunnels under London. The basic designs however, were very little different from those introduced to the Victoria Line but without the addition of Automatic Train Operation.

This edition takes the story on, a

further 10 years, including the allocation changes of the cars between the various lines just at the time when a technical revolution has taken place. The electronic age will change the way future rolling stock is controlled and operated and new practices will reduce the maintenance requirements so that rolling stock development is now again at a point of major change.

It has been my privilege to be present during my life time at the change from Gate stock requiring at least five men to

enable a train to roll to the new sophisticated stock with passenger door control and one-person operation of either sex. The story of the changes is contained in these pages. I have had the help of many people, mainly colleagues, in the development of this story over the years; some of these are now no longer available to thank, so that it is invidious for me to mention any particular names, but I am grateful to them all.

*J. Graeme Bruce*

# A Note of What Makes a Tube Train Go and Stop

From the beginning, tube trains have been propelled by direct current series traction motors, axle-mounted, and brought to a stop by compressed air acting on brake shoes rubbing on the tread of the road wheels. Apart from an improvement in the power/weight ratio, the traction motor has changed basically very little over the years.

The controls have become more sophisticated, allowing the traction motor to be used to provide electric braking, but the whole system however would still be recognised by the early pioneers as only a modification of their basic concept.

On the other hand, apart from the brake shoe itself, the method of controlling the compressed air pressure applying the brake shoes to the wheel tread has altered almost out of recognition, and attempts are now being made to avoid wheel tread braking altogether.

## The Traction Motor

A traction motor used on tube trains consists basically of two parts, a drum — called an armature — revolving inside a steel case provided with magnetic pole-pieces. All tube train traction motors have four poles provided with magnetising coils so connected that the poles are magnetised north and south alternately. The armature is provided with a number of insulated loops of copper bars which, during their rotation, pass underneath the magnetised pole-pieces. These armature coils, as they are called, are connected in series with the coils magnetising the poles, so that the same electrical current passes through both. It is for this reason that the traction motors are known as series type. When the current taken is heavy the magnetic fields are strongest and, therefore, the power output provided will be at its greatest. A characteristic feature of a dc series motor is that it gives its greatest output (torque) at starting.

The current is transferred to the armature by means of a commutator which consists of a complete drum of copper bars — insulated from each other — to which the armature coils are connected. Graphite brushes rub upon these commutator segments. As each bar passes under a brush, the current in the coil connected to it is reversed in direction as it passes out of the influence of a magnetic pole of one polarity into the influence of the other. Good commutation — as this process of the transfer of electricity at the commutator is called — is obtained when the brushes are placed in the exact magnetic neutral position between the poles.

Until the advent of commutating poles or interpoles in the design of traction motors, about 1907, sparking at the commutator, caused by the magnetic fields from the main poles being distorted by the fields set up by armature coils themselves, was an accepted problem. This phenomenon was understood because it is one of the fundamentals of electricity discovered by Michael Faraday. He found that where a current flows, a magnetic field is set up, and the direction of the field depends on the direction of the flow of current. Interpoles, which are additional poles with less turns in the coils for magnetising purposes than the main poles, are designed so as to compensate for the distortion of the field caused by the armature fields. These poles, sometimes called commutating poles because they are designed to assist commutation, are more usually known as interpoles because they are inserted between the main poles with their windings in series with the windings of the main poles. The provision of these interpoles helps to produce sparkless commutation at the brushes, because the same current which could produce the field distor-

*Below:*
**The mechanical governor and run back detector mounted on and driven by a trailer axle on 1967 Tube Stock ensures that the acceptable speed is not exceeded or that the train does not run back after being brought to a stand in a tunnel.** *LRT 68/978*

tion passes through them and provides an opposing field which corrects the distortion.

The solid blocks of graphite which rub on the commutator are called 'brushes' because, before the graphite block was introduced, the method used was virtually a brush made of copper wire.

The direction of rotation of a series-type direct current motor can be easily reversed, by reversing either the polarity of the field coils or the direction of the flow of current in the armature. Reversing tube trains has, until the advent of the Victoria Line stock, always been achieved by reversing the polarity of the field coils.

The motors for the 1967 Tube stock were designed to provide rheostatic braking which involved controlling the polarity of the main fields, and subsequent motor designs have included the requirement for electric braking.

**The Control**
Apart from the initial use of 500V dc as the traction supply system on the Central London and City & South London Railways, the power supply to the tube trains is nominally 600V dc, and this is used directly by the traction motors. However, if this current supply were applied to a stationary traction motor, a very heavy current would occur and damage would be done, so it is necessary to limit the current at starting. This is done by inserting resistances in series with the motor, and then cutting resistance out in steps as the motor speeds up, until the motor itself is across the 600V line.

In the very early days of electric traction, one traction motor was provided with a large rheostat which was operated by hand. Sometimes two traction motors were provided in series, so that one rheostat controlled two motors, and the first locomotives on the City & South London Railway had controls of this kind. The control known as series-parallel was then invented, and this has been used on tube trains ever since, including the later locomotives on the City & South London Railway.

The principle of series-parallel control is basically simple. In starting, two motors and a resistance are connected in series. The resistance is gradually reduced until the two motors alone in series are connected across the 600V line. Switching — called transition — is then arranged, connecting the two motors in parallel but re-inserting the resistance in series with the motors. The resistance is again cut out, until each motor is across the 600V line, when full speed is then obtained.

It is in the switching known as transition that the complication of the circuit arises. When the arrangement was first invented, the method adopted was known as open circuit transition.

With this method, at the notch beyond full series, the connection between the two motors was opened, and then reconnected in parallel with the resistance again inserted. This arrangement not only produced an agonising jerk in the running of the train, but also caused wear and tear on the switchgear because of the breaking of the circuit under load. To overcome the wear and tear, short-circuit transition was arranged whereby one motor was temporarily short-circuited with the resistance re-inserted before being disconnected and reconnected in parallel. This arrangement reduced considerably the current which had to be broken by the switchgear and reduced the hiatus in the acceleration of the train.

Finally introduced was bridge transition, which arranged the resistances and the two motors in the form of a bridge, so that the appropriate operation of switches connected the series and parallel and resistance steps without any electrical breaks being necessary at all. Bridge transition was so effective that once adopted it superseded all others. All tube traction control systems since 1920 have been provided with series-parallel control using bridge transition, and this system is still used today.

The multiple-unit system of control of electric trains was invented in America by Frank J. Sprague and tried out in Chicago in 1898. It is almost impossible to imagine the operation of a tube railway without the use of this basic system, which was adopted by the Central London Railway in 1903.

The first arrangement used a hand-operated controller which energised a group of wires running the complete length of the train as required. Each individual traction control equipment was connected to this group of train wires and responded to the position of the hand-operated controller in use at the time. These control wires energised switches on each car, cutting out the resistances and carrying out the transition steps.

Until 1936 all the switches used on tube trains were electro-magnetic, in that the control wires directly energised magnetic coils which closed and opened the appropriate switches. With hand-notching controllers, the position of the master controller handle determined the switches which were energised. If the controller was operated too rapidly, then an overload could be produced, resulting in the tripping out of the main circuit breakers. The equipment designed for Standard tube stock still used electro-magnetic switches, but incorporated an accelerating relay which held the 'message' from the master controller until the power circuit was receptive to the next step in the sequence. The driver was able to select one of three running positions — shunt, series, or parallel.

The actual switching became automatic, and thus, to some extent, outside his control.

In 1936 a new control system was introduced, the PCM from America, where it had been in use on the New York subways for some 10 years. In America the letters PCM originally stood for Pneumatic Camshaft Modified, but, as the version redesigned in England to suit London Transport conditions had remained basically unaltered from its inception, the letters have been accepted to mean Pneumatic Camshaft Motor. This system transferred most of the switching to contacts operated by a camshaft, turned by an air motor which was stopped and started under the control of an accelerating relay working on a notched wheel. In the original design used in America the moving force operating the camshaft was entirely pneumatic, but to avoid juddering, which occasionally occurred, oil was introduced on one side of the twin operating cylinders to make for smoother operation. This was the modification at which stage the design was introduced into England. A feature of the control which made for reliability of operation was that the camshaft turned in one direction to bring the switching to full series and then returned to the 'off' position. This also corresponded to full parallel in combination with another switch that performed the transition function. Under normal operation — after full acceleration has been achieved — there was no running back of the camshaft when the equipment was switched off. This type of equipment was modified to incorporate rheostatic braking so that the traction motors could be used as generators, and such equipments were fitted to 1967 and 1972 Tube stock, but controlling four motors instead of two. PCM control was also installed on the 1973 Tube stock, but this type of equipment will now be superseded to enable advantage to be taken of the devices known as 'choppers', utilising electronic techniques enabling regenerative braking in addition to rheostatic braking to be achieved. The control equipment provided on the 1983 Tube stock was the first tube stock equipment to provide for regeneration.

**The Westinghouse Brake**
George Westinghouse first introduced a compressed air brake in 1869, but it was not until he invented the triple valve in 1872 that the Westinghouse brake became superior to most of the other braking systems then in use.

The Westinghouse brake, including the triple valve, is fitted to all tube trains before 1973 Tube stock as the ultimate safety stopping medium, although latterly it was not used for normal braking. On 1973 Tube stock however the conventional Westinghouse pneumatic emergency brake was replaced by a fail-safe electro-pneumatic system.

The Westinghouse brake was used as the service brake on all tube trains until the introduction of the EP (electro-pneumatic) brake in 1930.

Apart from an operating handle and brake cylinders applying the brake shoes to the treads of the wheels, the Westinghouse brake consists of three devices on each vehicle — a brakepipe, an auxiliary reservoir, and a triple valve. The brake pipe is continuous throughout the train, and when fully charged the brakes are released and the train free to move.

When a brake application is required, air is released from the train brake pipe by means of the operating handle, which reduces the brakepipe pressure below that of the auxiliary reservoir. This imbalance of pressure makes the triple valve move and allows the air from the auxiliary reservoir to enter the brake cylinder to equalise the pressure. A small brakepipe pressure reduction gives a small brake application, while a large brakepipe pressure reduction would give a heavy brake application. The brake is released by recharging the brake pipe above that of the auxiliary reservoir, so that the triple valve moves back, releasing the air in the brake cylinder to atmosphere and enabling the auxiliary reservoir itself to be recharged to restore equilibrium. The triple valve is so named because it connects auxiliary reservoir, brake cylinder and brakepipe together. This braking system was easily adapted to include the numerous safety devices required on a tube train. The driver's deadman's handle, passenger emergency alarms, and the tripcock (which operates if a signal is passed at danger), all exhaust the brakepipe and cause the maximum possible brake application.

The fail-safe system that replaces the Westinghouse system in the more modern stock consists of a round-the-train wire, which is used to detect breakaways, passenger alarms and other items which require an emergency brake application, just as the loss of air in the Westinghouse brakepipe previously did.

### The EP Brake

One fundamental difficulty with the Westinghouse brake arises from the fact that it takes time for the brakepipe pressure to be reduced and for the triple valves to operate. In addition, all triple valves do not operate simultaneously, so that there can be a time-lag between the brakes applying on one car to another in the same train. The introduction of the electro-pneumatic brake, superimposed upon the Westinghouse brake, overcame this problem for normal service stops by utilising electrical circuits to apply the brake simultaneously on every car. Controlling valves permitted com-

pressed air from the main air-pressure pipe to enter or leave the brake cylinders independently of the action of the triple valve and without reducing the brakepipe pressure. The Westinghouse brake was retained for operation with all the safety features, but the normal service stops were controlled by electrically-operated valves. All tube trains constructed after 1930 were provided with EP brakes, until the 1973 Tube stock introduced the Westcode system.

Later a further device was added to the EP brake system, known as the retardation controller, which consists of two glass tubes mounted along the direction of travel of the train. These tubes contain mercury which, when the braking rate is excessive, cause contacts to be made by the pendulum effect of the mercury in the tube. The brake application is in this way cut off, and the retardation of the train kept down to the required limit. Thus the maximum braking rate can be used for service stopping, without the wheels locking and skidding. By this means some automatic compensation is built into the braking system for light and heavily loaded trains. The provision of this type of electrically-controlled braking system enables the automatic system of stopping trains on the Victoria Line to be used with the 1967 Tube stock. All the emergency features are still, however, applied to the Westinghouse brake, which provides

the ultimate 'fail-safe' brake system. Similar systems are applied to the 1972 Tube stock, which also incorporated rheostatic braking, blended with the EP brake.

On the 1973 Tube stock the service brake control is by the Westcode system. This controls the braking by selecting one of a number of steps of brake cylinder pressure, which is automatically adjusted on each car for passenger loading. Retardation control is replaced by wheelslide protection which detects wheel pick-up and automatically eases the brake pressure on that car temporarily.

The introduction of electric braking — that is the motors acting as generators to provide the retarding force — requires a sophisticated blending system between the compressed air brake and the electric brake, which ensures that the air brake takes over should the electric brake not pull its weight in the braking required. Tube trains so far have utilised the simplest form of electric brake — that is rheostatic braking in which the power produced by the motors is loaded on to resistances which dissipate this power in heat. The next stage is to provide regenerative braking, where the power produced can be absorbed in the supply system and therefore provide economies. No doubt the next generation of trains for tube working will enable this to be satisfactorily achieved without too much complication.

---

*Below:*
**Comparison of self-lapping electro-pneumatic brake controllers. The 1938 Tube Stock with rotary valve on the left and the 1959 Tube Stock with poppet valves on the right. The introduction of poppet valves reduced the amount of skilled maintenance required.**

# 1. The City & South London Railway

The 'Tube Age' began when the City & South London Railway was opened to traffic from Stockwell to King William Street in the City of London on 18 December 1890. Originally incorporated as the City of London & Southwark Subway in 1884, the name was subsequently changed to the City & South London Railway. After trials on part of the route in 1889 and 1890, the line was formally opened over the 3⅛ miles by the Prince of Wales (later King Edward VII) on 4 November 1890, but was not opened for public traffic until 18 December of the same year. The line had six stations — King William Street, Borough, Elephant & Castle, Kennington, Oval and Stockwell.

This line was the beginning of London's extensive deep-level tube system and, with the exception of King William Street, is still part of London's Underground. Originally designed for cable haulage, the twin circular tunnels ran under the street at an average depth of about 60ft from the surface. Without the provision of lifts a railway at this level would not have been successful. Twelve hydraulically-operated lifts — two at each of the six stations — were originally provided, capable of carrying 50 passengers. The first electric lift at an Underground station was installed in 1897 by Easton Anderson at Kennington. The power station at Stockwell contained three pumping engines

which supplied the hydraulic mains for the operation of the hydraulic lifts.

Originally designed for cable operation, two winding engines were to be installed at Elephant & Castle — one working north over the City section and the other driving the cable over the Stockwell section to the south. The tunnels north of Elephant & Castle were approximately 10ft 2in (3.099m) diameter while those south to Stockwell were 10ft 6in (3.2m). The difference in size was to provide for the higher speeds which were possible on the southern sections because the line of the track was less curved. The extra few inches were required to allow for what was known as the 'dynamic clearance'

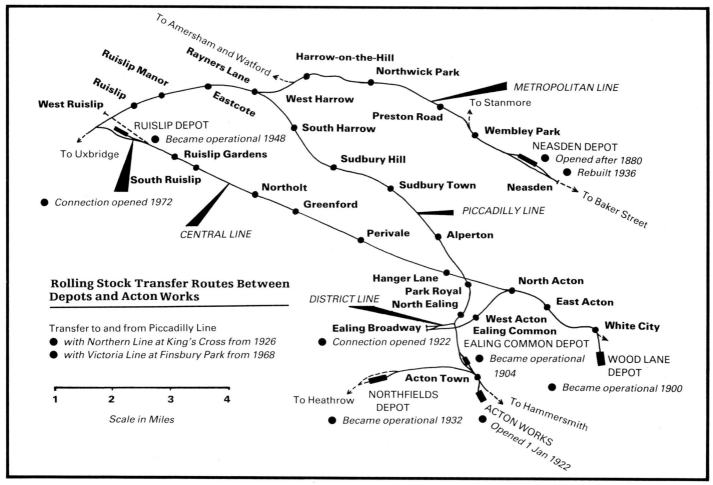

**Rolling Stock Transfer Routes Between Depots and Acton Works**

Transfer to and from Piccadilly Line
● with Northern Line at King's Cross from 1926
● with Victoria Line at Finsbury Park from 1968

Scale in Miles: 1  2  3  4

To Amersham and Watford
Rayners Lane
Harrow-on-the-Hill
Northwick Park
Ruislip Manor
Ruislip
West Ruislip
Eastcote
West Harrow
METROPOLITAN LINE
To Stanmore
Preston Road
RUISLIP DEPOT
● Became operational 1948
To Uxbridge
Ruislip Gardens
South Harrow
Wembley Park
NEASDEN DEPOT
● Opened after 1880
● Rebuilt 1936
South Ruislip
Sudbury Hill
Neasden
● Connection opened 1972
Northolt
Sudbury Town
To Baker Street
Greenford
PICCADILLY LINE
CENTRAL LINE
Perivale
Alperton
Hanger Lane
North Acton
Park Royal
DISTRICT LINE
North Ealing
East Acton
Ealing Broadway
West Acton
White City
Ealing Common
● Connection opened 1922
EALING COMMON DEPOT
WOOD LANE DEPOT
● Became operational 1904
● Became operational 1900
To Heathrow
Acton Town
NORTHFIELDS DEPOT
To Hammersmith
ACTON WORKS
Opened 1 Jan 1922
● Became operational 1932

— that is the extra swaying movement of the cars at the higher speeds. The City section was designed to cover working at 10mph while the Stockwell section cable was to be run at 12mph.

During the construction of the line the promoters considered the use of electric traction, which was then in its infancy. Although the tunnels (constructed of cast iron segments bolted together) were limited in size, standard gauge track was installed. This was constructed with 60lb flat-bottomed rail spiked to cross-sleepers resting on the tube segments without ballast, to avoid dust. The conductor rail, at 500V, was a flat inverted channel section placed between the running rails 1¼in (31.7mm) below running rail level and 1ft 3in (381mm) from the westerly-placed running rail; that is, not in the centre of the track. The rail was placed on glass insulators. A plank walkway 18in wide was placed in the remaining yard or so between the running rails.

The collector shoes were dished cast iron approximately 10in (254mm) square. Wooden ramps were provided to lift the collector shoes for overrunning the rails at points and crossings.

At Stockwell, where a 'scissors' crossing was provided in front of the two platform terminal, movable conducting bridges were installed; these were interlocked with the point levers to enable a continuous path to be presented to the collector shoes, to avoid sparking and gapping troubles. The terminal at King William Street was a single track terminal so that this elaborate arrangement was not required.

The approach to King William Street was round a sharp right-hand curve of 140ft (42.6m) radius with a section of 1 in 40. The southbound line fell at 1 in 14 to come below the northbound line. The southbound tube left King William Street in the normal left-hand position but then ran under the northbound tube, passing to the right-hand side of it and then recrossing again between Borough and Elephant & Castle stations. The tunnels had to be placed one on top of the other because of the narrowness of the streets in the city section and the need to avoid interference with private property on the surface, but the reason for the complete crossover is now obscure.

Most stations had two separate tunnels and platforms, which still exist today; King William Street was arranged with one line in the centre of the large single tunnel — the arrival platform where passengers left the train was on one side while the departure platform was on the other. The terminus at Stockwell had an island platform between two tracks. In 1895 King William Street station was rebuilt with an island platform and two roads with a scissors crossover.

The depot, located at Stockwell, contained a repair shop and carriage

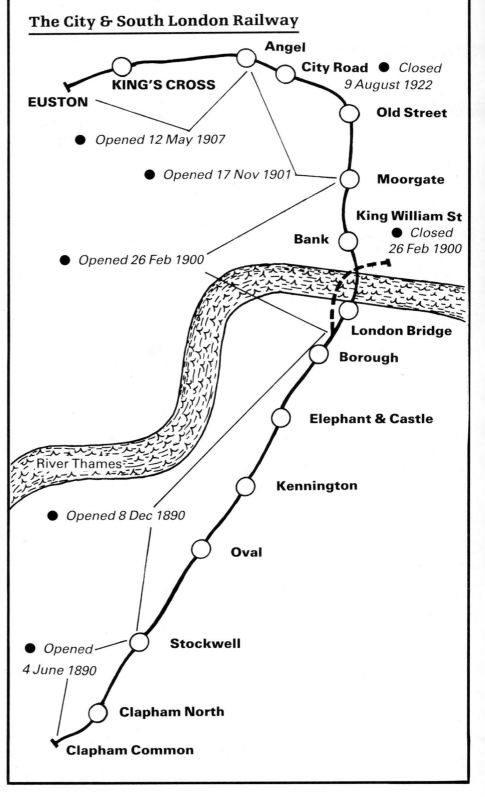

*Above:*
**The extent of the City & South London Railway at the time it was acquired by the Underground Group in 1913.**

*Above right:*
**A Crompton electric locomotive near the 20-ton hydraulic lift installed to raise the trains from the tunnel to the depot at Stockwell. This end view shows the proximity of the collector shoe to the coupler.** *LRT U3597*

*Right:*
**Diagram of the City & South London three-wire system where earth was the mid-point of a 1,000V dc generation system. One track was 500V above and the other track 500V negative to earth.**

shed as well as a generating station. It was placed on the surface and was approached by a 1 in 3½ incline from a curved spur off the southbound line at the north end of Stockwell station. The rolling stock was hauled up this incline by a steam winding engine. After a runaway accident on this ramp, a 20-ton Waygood hydraulic lift which could accommodate a complete carriage was installed in 1906.

On 25 February 1900 the line was extended northwards to Moorgate to make a new length of four miles with the section between the Borough and King William Street being abandoned. On 3 June 1900 a southern extension was added to Clapham Common. The rails on these and later extensions were 80lb/yd while the conductor rails were placed on porcelain insulators. Moorgate was only a temporary terminus, because on 17 November 1901 the line was extended again, to Angel. These extensions lengthened it to 6½ miles, finally reaching its maximum of 7¼ miles on 12 May 1907 when it was extended to Euston.

At first the power station supplied the power directly to the third rail, but after the extension to Clapham Common and Moorgate in 1900, sub-stations were introduced, utilising a three-wire system with 1,000V across the outer wires. The third rail on one track was positive and the other track negative with the running rails being the mid-point. To avoid connecting the two poles together, the scissors crossing and the two tracks at the terminal stations at either end were completely of one polarity with an adequate rail gap provided before each of the scissors crossings.

In 1900 a completely new and larger power house was built at the same

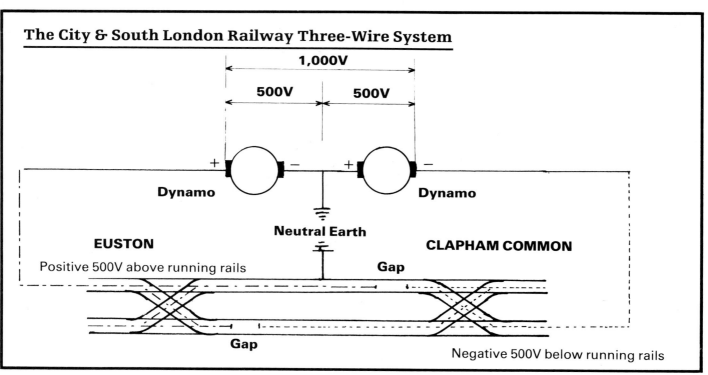

**The City & South London Railway Three-Wire System**

1,000V

500V     500V

+   Dynamo   −        +   Dynamo   −

Neutral Earth

EUSTON                    CLAPHAM COMMON

Positive 500V above running rails        Gap

Gap                    Negative 500V below running rails

location. North of Borough, two sub-stations were provided — one at London Bridge and the other at Angel — which were fed at 2,000V dc, one feeder at 1,000V above earth and the other 1,000V below earth. Rotary balancers were provided between these 'outer' feeders and neutral feeding the 500V conductor rails. The overall effect, probably unique, was that of a five-wire arrangement, the line south of London Bridge being fed on the more normal three-wire arrangement.

In 1913 the City & South London Railway was taken over by the Underground Electric Railways Co of London, and in 1915 the unique type of supply arrangement was discontinued, the supply subsequently being provided from the Underground power station at Lots Road through rotary converter

*Left:*
**One of the Crompton locomotives with wheels and traction motor removed, showing the gearless arrangement with the motor armature an integral part of the axle.**
*LRT U872*

*Below:*
**The interior of one of the early City & South London locomotives of 1890. The rotary control handle on the left works directly on the resistor connections while the air brake and handbrake handles are on the right.**

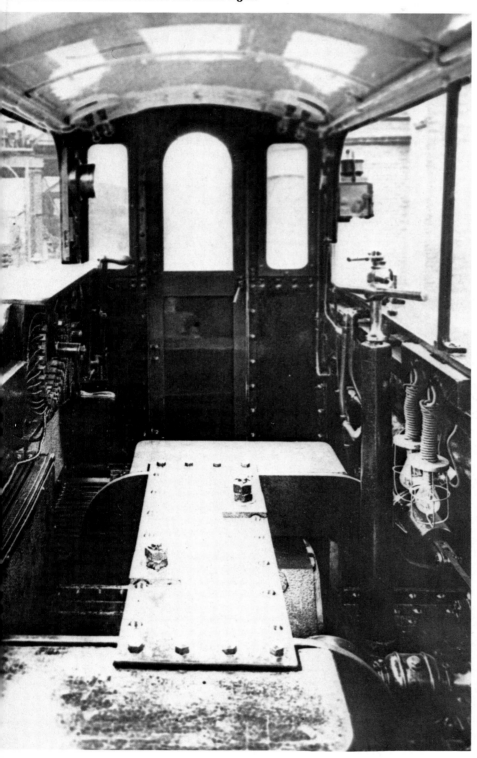

sub-stations with the conductor rail voltage raised from 500 to 550.

Due to the very limited experience with electric traction then available, it was necessary to use electric locomotives to haul the passenger cars. By December 1889 rails had been laid from the City to Borough and a temporary generating set was installed at Borough station. Trials were then conducted with one locomotive and two cars.

By the opening of the line in 1890 a total of 14 locomotives for operation in service had been provided by Mather & Platt Ltd, of Manchester, with the mechanical parts built by Beyer Peacock, also of Manchester. Original records show that a total of 16 locomotives were constructed, the original numbers 1 and 2 being duplicated. The first two locomotives were experimental: No 1 had gearless motors and was used with the two cars on the trial runs, while locomotive No 2 was fitted with geared motors, also for trials. Subsequently, a further 14 locomotives were built with the motors series-wound of the two-pole Edison-Hopkinson type. In outward appearance these locomotives resembled the steam tram dummies hauling tramcars then in use in several parts of the country. They were four-wheeled with plate frames, having 27in (686mm) diameter wheels in an overall length of 14ft (4.267m), a width of 6ft 10in (2.083m) and an overall height of 8ft 5½in (2.578m). The ends of the main plate frames supported a low-slung buffer beam carrying a link and pin coupler. It was this construction which necessitated the offset conductor rail, which had to clear this coupler.

In these early locomotives the two traction motors were wound directly on the two axles and were of the Gramme ring type, resembling a large ball of string. The magnetic pole-pieces of the motors were U-shaped, inclined at 45° over the axles. The two motors were connected permanently in series and controlled by a plain rheostat with 26 contacts. Reversing was achieved by a switch which changed the armature connections.

The locomotives were always at the leading end of the trains, and reversing at the terminals was achieved by stepping each locomotive back to the following train. A schedule speed would be about 11½mph and a maximum train speed was about 25mph, at which speed the motor armature (and, of course, the axle) was rotating at about 310rpm.

The locomotives were fitted with Westinghouse compressed air brakes as well as having a handbrake. Initially, no compressor was fitted, but the locomotives carried two long cylindrical reservoirs of about 18cu ft mounted under the side sheeting. These reservoirs were recharged during the Stockwell reversal from a compressed air line charged at 80lb/sq in. The power station contained twin air pumps for maintaining this supply. The recharging hose on the locomotive was mounted on the frame between the axles and the charge was a sufficient supply for at least 30 stops, more than ample to cover one round trip. The locomotives were also fitted with a powerful handbrake applied by a capstan-type handle. The air pipe was carried along the top of the carriages from a hosepipe connected to the locomotive.

In the working of the line it was found that 14 locomotives were insufficient and so two more locomotives were purchased from Siemens Bros of London. The essential difference introduced by these locomotives was that the armatures were drum-wound but still mounted directly on the axles.

The original livery was an unlined red-brown body, black frame and large polished brass number (and maker's plate) in the centre of each side sheet. On the end frames, below the floor level, were white-painted capitals 'CITY' and 'STOCKWELL', which at the time denoted the invariable destinations. By 1899 the livery had been changed to orange chrome in the form of three panels lined out with yellow edging and black borders. The frames were red-brown and the cab roofs were usually white.

Locomotive No 10 hauled the Royal opening train in 1890 and was subsequently named *Princess of Wales*, being provided with a special name-plate including the date, 4 November

1890. For a time this locomotive carried a special livery of cream and French grey.

In 1895 locomotive No 17 was constructed in the company's own workshops at Stockwell. Locomotives Nos 18, 19 and 20 were constructed by Crompton & Co, Electric Construction Co and Thames Ironworks respectively and delivered by 1898.

Locomotive No 17 was similar in construction to the Siemens Nos 15 and 16, but reverted to the Gramme ring armature in the motors. Tests were carried out with locomotives Nos 12, 15 and 17 to determine a future design of

locomotive for the extension lines which resulted in the construction of Nos 18, 19 and 20. They were provided with four-pole motors and series-parallel control, but the drum-type armatures were still mounted on the axles. In addition, an air compressor was fitted, but the locomotives were still provided with the charging connecting hose as well. Locomotive No 19 was also equipped with the Electric Construction Co's drum controller.

Experience gained with locomotives 18-20 led to the final design: Nos 21 and 22 were built at Stockwell while Nos 23-52 were completed by Crompton

*Below:*
**One of the original locomotives — No 8 — after reconstruction, which included the fitting of axle-hung traction motors and gear drive.** *LRT U871*

*Right:*
**Electric locomotive No 36 (built by Crompton in 1900) is seen together with car No 30, one of the original 'padded cells' built by Ashbury. This picture shows the brakepipe coupling between the locomotive and the train at roof level. The trellis gates on the end platform at the locomotive end and the Bostwick gates between cars are attached to the bogie frames.** *LRT U3595*

& Co, which received the main contract.

By 1907 the line had reached its maximum under locomotive haulage, extending from Euston to Clapham Common, and the fleet consisted of some 52 locomotives. By this time all the later locomotives had series parallel control of two traction motors, nose-suspended, driving the axles through single reduction gearing.

Between 1904 and 1907, 10 of the original locomotives Nos 3-12 had been completely rebuilt, including the replacement of the electrical equipment by the BTH company. Two GE74-type nose-suspended geared motors were fitted together with a tramway type series-parallel drum controller with reversing spindle. In 1912 locomotive No 22 was fitted with two GE211 motors which were provided with interpoles. The further introduction of this type of motor was curtailed by World War 1.

In June 1913 it is on record that 45 locomotives were in maintenance and 37 were required to work a full weekday service, but by 1920 Nos 2, 13 and 14 had been scrapped and No 1 was withdrawn and stored for preservation. It is suspected, however, that No 1 (now preserved in the Science Museum) is either No 13 or No 14 as it does not conform to the original description of locomotive No 1, but does follow that of Nos 3-14.

The line opened in 1890 with 10 three-car trains. The first 30 passenger cars were built by the Ashbury Railway Carriage & Iron Co. These original vehicles had bodies 26ft (7.92m) long, 6ft 10in (2.08m) wide and 8ft 4½in (2.55m) high from rail level. The overall length of the cars, however, was 32ft

(9.75m) as each bogie carried a semi-circular extension to the outer end of its frame, projecting beyond the car body. These original vehicles earned the soubriquet 'padded cell' because they were provided only with a number of ventilating slits about 6in (152mm) deep with alternate ones glazed just below the gutter line, as well as high-backed longitudinal padded seats. The line was entirely in tunnel, so it was thought that as there was nothing to look at there was no need to provide windows since the conductors were required to announce the station names. Nevertheless, public opinion was against the continuation of this arrangement, so that subsequent batches of cars were provided with sidelights and the original cars were converted.

Initially, there was no provision for standing passengers but, subsequently, wooden rails holding a total of 16 straps were fixed to the clerestory roof. One car in each train was labelled 'smoking', and in the early days ladies were not permitted to travel in these cars. Also, an early notice forbade passengers from riding on the roof.

The bodies were carried on two four-wheeled bogies which carried a semi-circular extension on the outer end of its frame projecting beyond the car body. The outer end of the bogies carried a low-slung buffer beam to which was fixed a link and pin coupler.

The bodies had floors about 1ft 6in (457mm) from rail level, the space under the seats receiving the wheels and, in the middle, the Westinghouse brake cylinders and auxiliary reservoirs. At the ends of the cars were double sliding doors, opening to the

end platforms. At first these doors had wooden panels, but later the upper sections were glazed and 'hit and miss' ventilators introduced. The spaces between the cars were filled by single platforms resting on the bogie extensions; these were enclosed by manually operated Bostwick sliding lattice gates. The bogie extensions at the end of the rakes had small platforms with little iron fences at the corners and chains across the openings, although these end platforms were not normally used by passengers.

The headroom was over 6ft (1.829m) in the centre of the cars. Longitudinal seats for 32 passengers, 16 on each side, were provided, and these were divided by a transverse centre partition (without a door) into two sections of eight seats. The space under the seat was utilised by the wheels of the bogies which when full size were 2ft (610mm) in diameter, so that they normally projected 6in (152mm) above the passenger floor level. This is a design feature which has been passed on to all tube rolling stock which has been built subsequently.

Initially the trains were made up into three-car sets and carried two guards as well as a driver and assistant. The passengers normally did not use the end platforms, either at the locomotive end or at the rear end of the train. The guard or conductor closed and opened the end doors of both adjacent cars at his platform and attended to the gates. The front guard or conductor received a hand signal from the rear guard and then blew a whistle for the driver to start the train. One whistle for the northbound road and two whistles for the southbound road were used for

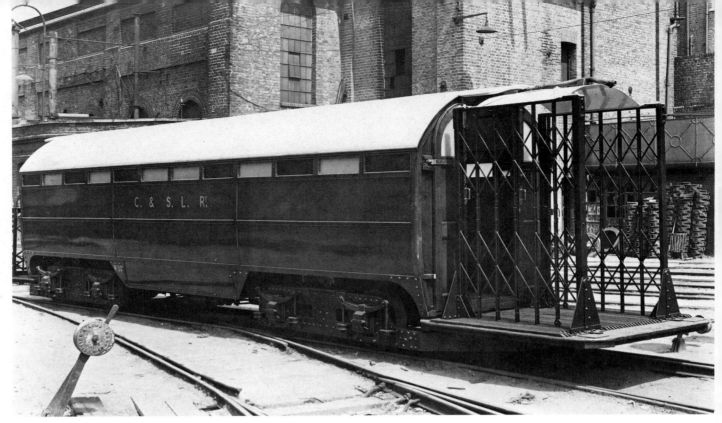

clarity, because island platforms could have trains for both directions at the same platform at the same time. For a few years the conductors worked enamelled indicator plates announcing the next station, which showed through an oblong opening in the end doors of the coaches.

A variety of car builders contributed to the total fleet of City & South London passenger cars but the basic design remained virtually unaltered, although each builder produced distinctive features. The differences were easily recognisable and were mainly in the size and shape of the windows. Four electric lights were provided with shades and in the later cars a further two bulbs were provided in the centre-line of the ceiling. The total illumination by these carbon filament lamps was about 64 candle power at its brightest. In addition, two emergency oil lamps were carried inside the car bodies. Gas lighting was used initially in the stations, there being insufficient power to provide a general electric lighting supply until more generation capacity was installed. In addition, the signals were provided with oil lamps, but these were often blown out by the passage of the trains so that by 1895 they had been replaced with electric signal lamps.

In 1893 outer home signals were fitted with an electrical release system. A brush contact was fitted to the last bogie of each train to give the indication of the passage of the last vehicle by making contact with a piece of insulated rail.

Traffic continued to rise with the universal fare set at 2d, passengers paying their money at turnstiles. This

system was abandoned after the opening of the Moorgate extension, when station-to-station fares were introduced. While only a single reversing platform existed at King William Street, neither additional trains nor lengthening beyond three cars could be arranged. A double platform was brought into use in 1895 but four-car trains could still not be operated, so it was decided to abandon King William Street and extend the line to Moorgate.

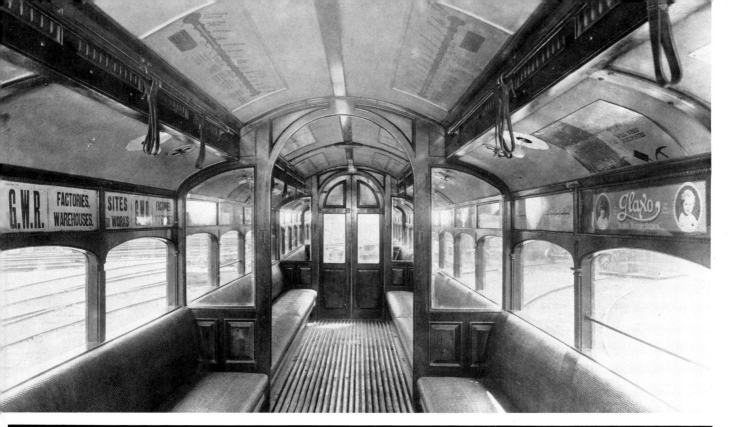

## City & South London and Yerkes Tubes

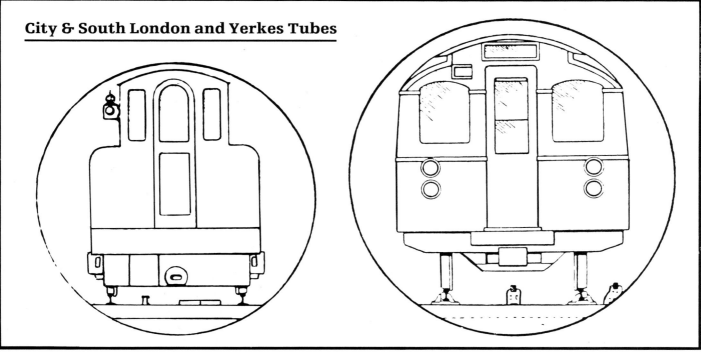

*Top:*
**An interior view of a subsequent City & South London car provided with windows, rattan-type seating and leather hand straps for standing passengers.** *LRT U820*

*Above:*
**Diagram showing the relative size of the original City & South London Railway tube against the Yerkes tube diameter, in particular indicating the comparison between the train profiles that necessitated the rebuild completed in 1926.**

This extension was opened in 1900 and subsequently four-car trains were operated.

By 1899, in preparation for the extensions of 1900, 10 more three-car trains were obtained from Hurst Nelson & Co, bringing the total number of cars up to 84. Previous batches had been obtained from the Bristol Carriage & Wagon Co, the Oldbury Carriage & Wagon Co and G. F. Milnes & Co. In general, the cars of the same build were kept together in sets. In 1901 further cars were added, mostly from G. F. Milnes & Co, until the number reached 140 cars.

By this time the trains were operating in four-car sets. The possibility of operating four-car trains had been considered in 1893, but the city terminus had only been able to accept four cars without the locomotive, so approval was obtained from the Board of Trade for the operation of motor coach trains. Trials with the experimental train were unsatisfactory because changing ends at peak periods proved much more time-consuming than the locomotive changing, and the arrangement was allowed to lapse.

When four-car trains were operated in order to run without additional crewing the central gangway was sometimes not manned and the gates secured. The end doors of the cars leading to this gangway were also securely locked. When five-car trains were later operated, one gangway was always not manned.

A further 33 cars came from the Brush Electrical Engineering Co in 1906/07, nominally all-steel, having a steel frame and panelling which was grained to match the wooden teak mouldings. These cars were now made up into five-car sets, the maximum length of trains operated by the City & South London Railway in its original form, and brought the fleet up to 165.

The Euston terminus was provided with a single siding south of the scissors crossing but in addition had a locomotive traverser just north of the station; thus a locomotive could run round its train before the adjacent platform was occupied. In spite of this it was normal to retain spare working locomotives at Euston, Angel, Moorgate, Elephant, Stockwell and Clapham Common during peak services, at which stations at least locomotive spur sidings were provided. The maximum service was operated by 32 trains and

38 locomotives which meant that there were five cars and six locomotives above the operational requirements, assuming that only 44 of the original 52 locomotives were then operational.

On 8 August 1922 the line beyond Moorgate was closed while the section to the south remained open to traffic between about 6am and 8pm. Stockwell and Borough stations were closed and — because the sidings at Stockwell were needed for works trains — the old route from Borough Junction to King William Street was used for berthing out-of-service stock that could not be accommodated in the running tunnels north of Moorgate.

Work proceeded on enlarging the tunnels, with a limited service being operated, but unfortunately on 27 November 1923 a board holding back some gravel in the new workings gave way and the tunnel became blocked. This resulting ingress of debris caused a serious disruption of the service. The line was shut down until 1 December 1924 when a service between Moorgate and Clapham Common again became possible.

A number of the cars were converted into flat cars to form 'muck' trains to work in the tunnel during the reconstruction. Twenty-two of the cars were converted to battery cars for certain of the workings to enable the locomotives

to work over sections where City & South London type current rails were no longer available because part of the reconstruction work was converting the railway to what had now become the London Underground four-rail collection system. As many as 16 'muck' trains could be working at one time in the tunnel during the reconstruction. The electric locomotives were disposed of in 1925 when the special works trains were no longer required.

A number of the cars were sold for various purposes in bungalow towns and as adjuncts to sports grounds, while No 30 (which was part of set No 10) was preserved and was exhibited at the Railway Museum at York for several years. This Ashbury-built car, restored as a 'padded cell', was subsequently transferred to London and is now among the collection at the London Transport Museum at Covent Garden.

The official preservation of 'No 1' locomotive, a Mather & Platt product which was possibly actually either No 13 or No 14 renumbered, is now an exhibit at the Science Museum. For some years the Underground kept locomotive No 36 for exhibition purposes. It was subsequently placed on a plinth on the concourse behind the terminal platforms of Moorgate (Metropolitan) station but was badly damaged by bombing in 1940. After the war restoration was not considered justified and the locomotive was broken up, although electrical parts (including the motors) were presented to Crompton Parkinson Ltd, the successor to Crompton & Co which built the locomotive.

*Below:*
**'No 1' locomotive being delivered to the Science Museum at South Kensington in London.** *LRT*

# 2. The Waterloo & City Railway

The success of the City & South London Railway caused the directors of the London & South Western Railway to reconsider their plans for providing a communication between Waterloo station and the City. Parliamentary powers were obtained in 1893 for the construction of the Waterloo & City Railway, the second tube railway to be built in London.

Although the railway is a tube, its close association with the London & South Western Railway (later the Southern Railway), coupled with its isolation, has kept it as a separate entity from London Transport. Nevertheless, the Waterloo & City Railway — still not an integral part of London's tube network — has played some part in the development of tube trains and so must be included in any review of London's Underground system.

Initially a special power station was constructed at Waterloo containing six Bell & Morcom high speed engines coupled to Siemens direct current generators producing the 500V supply. The line was constructed mainly with twin tubes, having an internal diameter of 12ft 1½in (3.696m) with some fairly sharp curves. Beyond the station at Waterloo were provided a series of sidings which acted as the depot for the trains, and a lift provided access to the main line from a spur tunnel line above which left the up line just beyond the Waterloo platform. This lift was normally positioned at the Waterloo & City level so special safeguards were

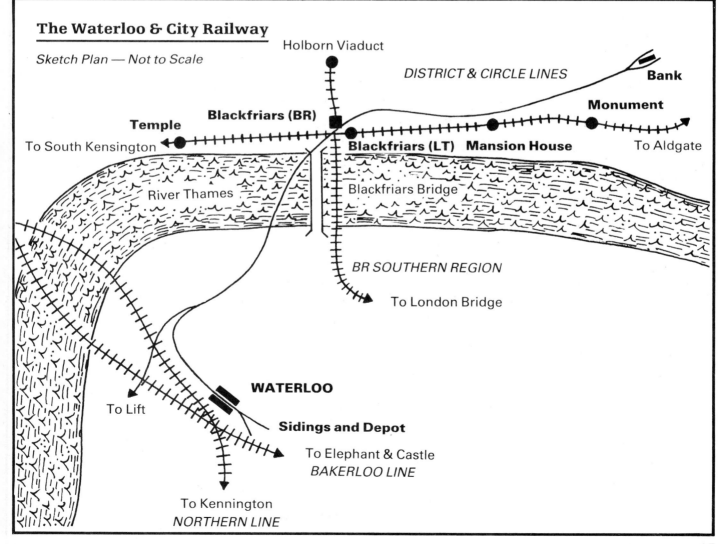

The Waterloo & City Railway

*Sketch Plan — Not to Scale*

# The Waterloo & City Railway

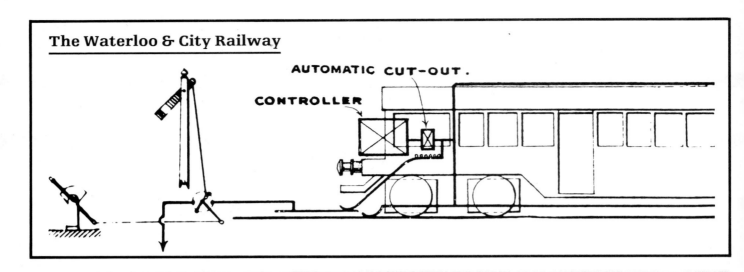

employed on the surface to prevent unauthorised cars or wagons gaining entrance to the lift shaft. One important function of the lift was the conveyance of coal wagons from the surface to the power station, which was reached from the depot sidings by a second smaller lift.

The line was opened to traffic on 8 August 1898. The power was supplied to the trains, which ran in the twin circular tunnels on a standard gauge track, by means of a centre conductor rail, the top surface of which was at the same level as the running rails. The voltage provided by the direct current supply between this rail and the running rails was a nominal 500V. The collector shoes were lifted over the running rails at points and crossings by means of hardwood ramps raising the undersurface 1½in (38mm) above the running rails. The collector shoes on the motor coaches were 40ft (12.19m)

*Top:*
**Diagram showing the safety system originally arranged for the early stock on the Waterloo & City if the signal was at danger.**

*Above:*
**One of the five motor cars built by Dick Kerr to operate during non-rush hours as single units.**

*Above right:*
**The driver's controller and brake valve on a Waterloo & City motorcar of 1898.**

*Right:*
**The driver's controller of 1898 stock. The reversing lever is at the bottom.**

apart but there were some gaps which could be greater than this so that it was necessary to have a bus line connecting together the shoes on the two motor cars of the train to prevent gapping.

The potential of the current rail was raised in April 1917 to a nominal 600V when the supply was obtained from the railway power station, which was built at Durnsford Road, through a rotary

converter sub-station at Waterloo. The original power house was then closed down.

The original rolling stock purchased for the line consisted of five four-car trains with bodies built by Jackson & Sharpe of Wilmington, Delaware, USA. The bogies were constructed at the Eastleigh carriage works of the London & South Western Railway and the

electrical equipment for the trains was provided by Siemens Bros & Co Ltd. Subsequently the trains were increased in length to five cars by the provision of additional trailer cars. In 1899 five double-ended single motor cars were built by Dick Kerr to provide the off-peak services. These cars were basically similar to the original vehicles except they had driving cabs at both ends. They also were fitted with two nose-hung single-reduction geared motors and tramcar-type drum controllers providing series-parallel connections. End doors were not possible on these cars so two side doors were provided at the end of the centre part of the cars.

The trains were formed into sets having at each end a motor car, with driving cabs at the outer ends only. The motor coaches seated 46 passengers and the trailers 56 passengers on

## 1898 Stock Motor Bogie and Frame

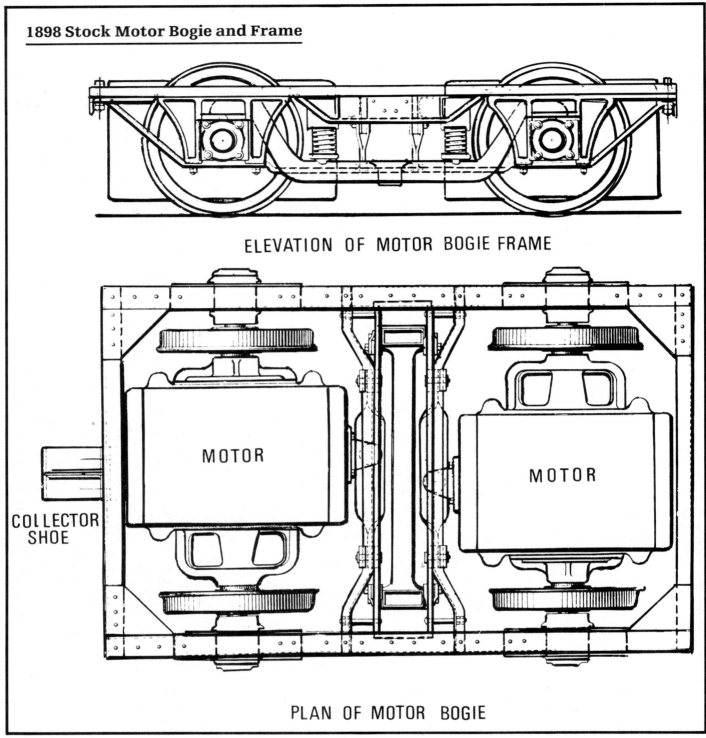

ELEVATION OF MOTOR BOGIE FRAME

COLLECTOR SHOE

MOTOR

MOTOR

PLAN OF MOTOR BOGIE

wooden seats without any upholstery. Placed over the trailing bogies of the motor cars and both bogies of the trailer cars were six seats on each side facing inwards. This arrangement gave running clearance for the bogie wheels. Over the motor bogies behind the driving cab there was a raised platform gained by ascending one intermediate step containing three seats on each side, also placed longitudinally. The seats in the centre of both the motor and trailer cars were in five sets of facing pairs except that in the motor cars one seat was omitted at the cab end on each side to provide access to a side door. The normal floor height was

1ft 10in (559mm) above rail level but the raised floor over the motor bogie was 3ft 2½in (978mm) above rail level.

The end bogie of each motor car carried two motors with the armatures wound on the axle, providing a gearless drive. The magnets of the motors were of cast steel providing four poles, two wound with series coils and two being consequent without any windings. Another unique feature was that the coils of the poles were in parallel with each other but both in series with the armature. All four motors were started in series and the final running position was a parallel group of two pairs of motors in series. It had been intended

that a further running position would have been all motors in parallel, and switching on the controller was originally provided for this. However, the Board of Trade railway inspector applied a speed limit which, together with the power house being unable to cope with the open-circuit transition with non-automatic acceleration, rendered the need for this arrangement unnecessary, and the controllers were modified accordingly.

The controller was of a unique design, because not only did it cater for series-parallel but had to arrange this for four motors. Arcing on the controller was reduced by a special breaking switch with carbon blocks which was arranged to open when the main circuit needed to be opened before either the connecting contacts were made or broken.

The reversing switch had three positions, forward, backwards and intermediate. In the latter position the controller was locked in the off position but the motors on that car were so connected that they secured power and control from the other end controller. The reversing key could only be withdrawn when the drum was in the intermediate position. These controllers were cumbersome, being operated by hand wheels, and had eight running positions.

In order to give complete control of the grouping of the motors as well as their direction of rotation, each motor had to have four leads — two for the armature and two for the fields connected to the controller — so that eight power leads were required to run the length of the train for this purpose. In addition there were three more same-sized ones connecting the collector shoes together, making 11 in all. These

*Above:*
**The motor bogie and motor removed from 1898 stock.**

*Below:*
**The interior of a Jackson & Sharp motor car, with the raised section above the motor bogie at the extreme end.** *Museum of British Transport A2897*

*Above:*
**A five-car train of Waterloo & City stock as delivered in 1940.** *British Railways Board*

*Above right:*
**The interior of a 1940 Waterloo & City motor car looking towards the driver's cab.**

*Right:*
**The old Waterloo & City stock being removed and the new stock being delivered in autumn 1940.** *British Museum of Transport C10969*

cables were run along the top of cars, and the Waterloo & City remained the only tube line constructed where this arrangement was permitted. Two collector shoes running on the centre conductor rail were carried on each motor car; these were connected together and then with those in the motor cars at the other end of the train, by the cables carried across the car roofs.

The cars were originally lit by carbon-filament lamps of 16 candle power run off the 500V system. Four lamps were run in series. Trailer cars had eight lamps inside while motor cars had seven, plus two in the driver's cab and two as headlights. Two oil lamps were also carried inside each car and there were additional ones at the ends of the trains.

Again on the Waterloo & City Line, the trains were equipped with Westinghouse continuous compressed air brake, but the air supply was not provided by a train-fitted air compressor; 30cu ft air reservoirs which were charged initially at 100lb/sq in were carried in each car. It was considered that this pressure in the train reservoir connecting lines would not fall below 70lb/sq in until 20 single journeys of the train had been completed, when a recharge from a standpipe in the lay-by siding was necessary. The train, of course, carried a second air pipe the whole length of the train for the Westinghouse brake operation.

The stationary compressor plant consisted of a battery of air pumps which delivered air at 140lb/sq in to a large reservoir connected to the standpipes in the sidings.

Owing to the nature of the line it was not possible to provide catch-points, but instead an ingenious arrangement to avoid collisions should a train pass a signal at danger was provided. At each signal a 'slipper' bar was placed on the outside of the track which made contact with a slipper, an insulated contact carried on the left side of the motor bogie. Fitted to the main circuit breaker was a tripping coil, wound to take the full 500V supply, which when energised released the catch. One end of the coil was connected to the slipper and the other to the positive power cable. The slipper bar was a piece of conductor rail connected to earth through a contact on the signal gear. Slipper bars permanently earthed were placed at the entrance to the Bank platforms and at Waterloo at the entrance to the sidings.

The whole of the original stock, signals and operating arrangement,

continued working until 25 October 1940 when the line was closed for three days to allow the rehabilitation of the line and new trains to be installed.

The English Electric Co, successor to Dick Kerr & Co, supplied 12 motor cars and 16 trailer cars formed into five-car trains each consisting of two motor cars and three trailers, the off-peak being operated by double-ended motor cars. A driving cab was located at both ends but only one motor bogie carrying two motors was provided, above which was a switch compartment. The power supply was still taken from a conductor rail but this had now been moved to the standard position outside the running rails. The slipper rail was replaced by a train stop and tripcock arrangement similar to that used on the Underground trains.

Control was now arranged by electro-pneumatic (EP) unit switches and the series-parallel connections were under the control of an automatic accelerating relay. The control supply was obtained from a potentiometer providing 70V. The supply to the potentiometer passed

*Above:*
**A Waterloo & City car disappearing down the lift to the railway below.**
*British Railways Board*

through the 'deadman' control contacts.

Half the car lights were fed from each end as there were now no through power lines, each motor car picking up its own current. The lighting switch on each motor car fed only the circuit supplied from that car. In order that the motor cars could be operated as single units with all car lights illuminated, a pneumatic interlock controlled from the hose coupling connected the two lighting circuits together when there was a lack of air at both ends of the coupling connectors. Each motor car was equipped with a 12V battery for emergency lighting in case of failure of the main supply.

Electrically-controlled air-operated

doors were a standard fitment on all the cars with the position switches in each cab, the guard working from the rear controls. As the trains were manned by a driver and a guard, single manning would require a major rearrangement of controls and wiring. Two sets of double-leaf sliding doors were provided in the trailer cars while the motor cars had one set of double doors and one single door adjacent to the motor bogie. The motor cars seated 40 passengers and the trailer cars 52 within an

overall length of 49ft 2in (1.499m) and width of 8ft 8in (2.64m) for both cars.

Originally, tickets were issued at turnstiles but subsequently authority to operate with only one guard was not given so the station staff were withdrawn and tickets issued on the trains. With the introduction of the new stock the booking of tickets on the trains was discontinued and automatic ticket machines and booking offices were installed at both Waterloo and the Bank.

# 3.  The Central London Railway

A line six miles long of standard gauge with a centre positive conductor rail at a potential of 500V, the Central London Railway was opened between Shepherd's Bush and Bank in 1900. During the first week of service the *Daily Mail* dubbed the line the 'Twopenny Tube' because of the uniform fare, a nickname which remained popular for many years, even after the uniform fare of 2d was discontinued in July 1907.

The Central London Railway was the first example of a railway electric traction system in Europe to provide a power station generating three-phase alternating current supplying substations. There conversion by rotary converter to direct current took place to feed the current rail.

To assist the trains to accelerate and to stop, the force of gravity was harnessed by placing the passenger stations on the top of rises, with gradients of 1 in 30 down out of the station and 1 in 60 up approaching the stations. This natural form of 'regeneration' is an arrangement still considered to be an asset in underground railway construction.

The platforms for the Central London Railway as originally constructed were 325ft (129.06m) long so that longer trains than those operating on the first two tube railways in London were proposed from the beginning. Initially it was proposed that each train would be hauled by two locomotives, one at each end with through power controls, but the Board of Trade Inspecting Officers had decided that through bus lines carrying power connectors should not be used in tube railways. It was therefore necessary to use one locomotive only, but powerful enough to haul the heaviest train.

The Prince of Wales (later King Edward VII) formally opened the Central London Railway on 27 June 1900, but the public passenger service did not begin until 30 July 1900.

Although the British Thomson Houston (BTH) Co Ltd received the entire electrical contract for the railway, the original locomotives were designed and built in America by the General Electric Co of Schenectady with which the BTH company was at that time associated. Originally 32 locomotives were ordered but only 28 were in fact built. It is assumed that the extra four would have been required for the extension beyond the Bank to Liverpool Street for which authority had already been obtained, but multiple-units had replaced locomotive working when this section was opened.

The locomotives were of heavy construction with a steeple cab, sometimes described as 'camel backed'. They were 30ft (9.14m) long over the buffers, the body length being 26ft 7in (8.1m) placed on two bogies, so that in modern parlance the arrangement was Bo-Bo because each of the four axles supported a GE56A-type gearless motor of nominal 117hp. An unusual feature of the locomotives was the divided end 'bonnets' containing the resistances, compressor and other control gear. The gangway thus provided enabled the locomotive crew to move into the train if necessary.

The locomotives weighed 44 tons, of which as much as 33 tons was unsprung since the motor armatures were built on the axles and the heavy motor frames were carried entirely by the axles. The armature shafts of the motors were actually hollow and pressed over the axles. The four motors drove wheels 3ft 6in (1.067m) in diameter when newly tyred. At starting the four motors were placed in parallel in pairs and the pairs in series.

The cab floor was in a well between the raised parts of the frames over the motor bogies. The single controller used for both directions of running was placed in a centre position of the cab. This large drum controller had nine series and seven parallel notches with open circuit transition. The controller handle was about 2ft (610mm) long and had a button release which assisted the driver to move it notch by notch. It could be removed and replaced 180° from its orignal position so the driver could stand in the same relative position for each direction of operation of the locomotive. However, because only one Westinghouse brake valve was provided, advantage of this facility was

*Below:*
**Wood Lane power house as established in 1900 for the Central London Railway. The alternators, driven by steam engines provided power at 25 cycles per second (Hertz) for distribution for conversion to 500V dc at sub-stations along the line.**

not always taken because of the difficulty of reaching the brake handle. The reverser, a horizontal drum under the main barrel, was worked by a long vertical lever. Under the central buffer on the locomotive a receiving shank was provided for the link and pin coupling. At first oil headlamps were used but later a powerful electric headlamp was mounted on one bonnet at each end.

Gearing for locomotive drives in 1900 was only in the experimental stage and was decreed to be too noisy for use in deep-level tube tunnels. However, the great unsprung weight of the loco-motives on the track combined with the very flexible bridge type rail caused serious complaints from property owners almost immediately after the line opened. Therefore train speeds were reduced by imposing series-only running, and a Board of Trade enquiry resulted in a report which was unsatis-factory to the railway company. It stated that 'Vibration sufficient to cause serious annoyance is actually felt in many of the houses situated along the course of the railway'. By August 1901 tests had been made with three locomotives rebuilt with geared nose-suspended motors of Type GE55, for this purpose having been equipped with new bogies which reduced the unsprung weight to 11 tons. The vibra-tion problem was thus reduced.

The 170 wooden trailer cars built in 1900/01 came from two car builders, the Ashbury Railway Carriage & Iron Co which provided 145 and the Brush Electrical Engineering Co of Loughbo-rough which provided 25. These cars were originally numbered 1 to 170.

The Central London tunnels were built to a general diameter of 11ft 6in (3.505m) so that a greater loading gauge than that on the City & South London Railway was permitted. The cars had wooden bodies 39ft (11.89m) long on underframes of 45ft 6in (13.87m) bear-ing end platforms of 3ft 3in (991mm) at both ends, to which access was gained from the car body by double sliding doors. The cars were 9ft 4½in (2.851m) high and 8ft 6in (2.591m) wide. They had bogies of 5ft (1.524m) wheelbase and passenger seats for 48.

The ends of the body were provided with longitudinal seats, 16 per side, these seats being placed over the bogies, the wheels projecting above floor level into the seat wells, an arrangement which has now become standard practice in all tube car construction. A further 16 seats were placed transversely in the centre of the cars in two sets of two by two. Moquette upholstery was provided, an unusual feature in urban transport at the time. The car used by the Prince of Wales for the opening ceremony was equipped with a floral design while the bulk of the cars had plainer material. Each seat was divided from its neigh-

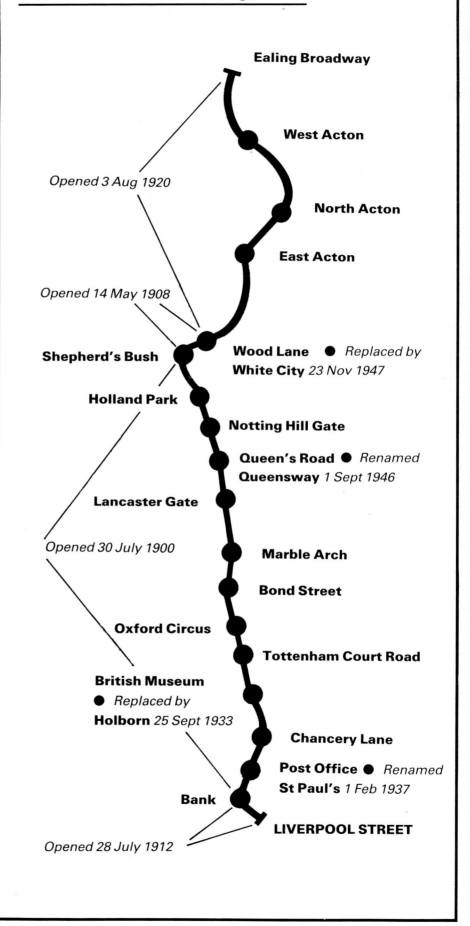

### The Central London Railway in 1920

Ealing Broadway

West Acton

North Acton

East Acton

*Opened 3 Aug 1920*

*Opened 14 May 1908*

Shepherd's Bush

Wood Lane ● *Replaced by* White City *23 Nov 1947*

Holland Park

Notting Hill Gate

Queen's Road ● *Renamed* Queensway *1 Sept 1946*

Lancaster Gate

*Opened 30 July 1900*

Marble Arch

Bond Street

Oxford Circus

Tottenham Court Road

British Museum ● *Replaced by* Holborn *25 Sept 1933*

Chancery Lane

Post Office ● *Renamed* St Paul's *1 Feb 1937*

Bank

LIVERPOOL STREET

*Opened 28 July 1912*

# The Central Line

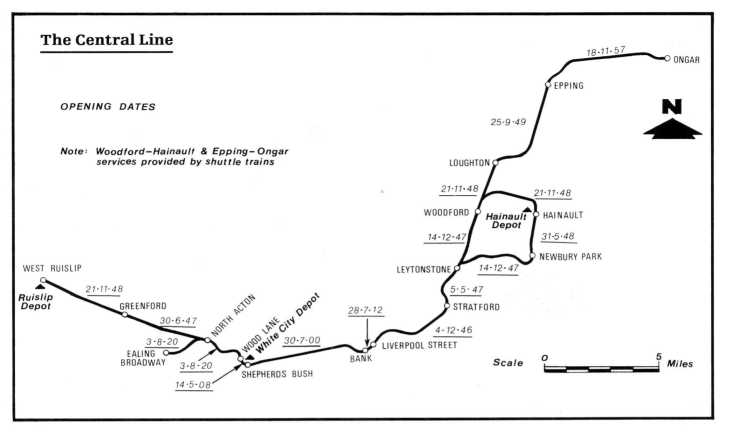

OPENING DATES

Note: Woodford–Hainault & Epping–Ongar
services provided by shuttle trains

*Above and below:*
**Central London locomotives No 12, the last one of the breed, outside Wood Lane depot.**

bour by an armrest on the longitudinal seating. Another unusual feature was the provision of basket-type racks and hat racks, and the lamps had shades. The double sliding doors were originally wood-panelled but subsequently were fitted with glass so that the gatemen could see into the car interiors to discourage beggars and itinerant musicians from annoying passengers.

The end platforms were surrounded by iron grille fencing with a 3ft 4in (1.016m) opening at the end over the buffer beam. The sides of these end platforms were closed by a swing gate having the hinge towards the end of the vehicle, allowing the gate to open inwards.

The trains were originally made up of sets of seven or six cars, with a locomotive and six or five gatemen riding between the cars to operate the gates. Only the end cars of the trains were 'smoking' cars and they were distinguished at first by 'stick-on' labels on the end waist panels. Later, 'smoking' boards were used and brackets were placed on all cars to secure these as required.

The starting of the trains from station platforms provided an interesting comparison with today's practice. When the intermediate conductors had closed their gates they held out a hand, the front conductor showed a green light to the rear and the rear conductor then showed a green light forward, which was repeated by the front conductor to the driver or second man on the locomotive.

Eight men were actually carried on a seven-car formation: two in the front

# A Central London Railway Locomotive

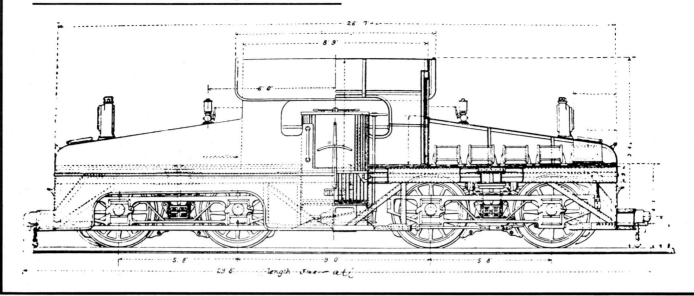

on the locomotive, a front and rear guard and four gatemen. At the terminals a locomotive stood spare to couple to the train for the return journey. It was the secondman's duty on the locomotives to carry out the coupling and uncoupling with link and pin type couplers. This coupling duty was a little hazardous as the man on the track was required to remain between the vehicles to drop the pin into position when the two portions of the coupler came together. At uncoupling the cars had to be squeezed together to enable the pin to be withdrawn. The brake pipe connection was at waist level of the cars but the lighting jumper was carried under the canopy of the cars. The end of the trains carried two electric tail lamps at canopy level as well as an oil tail lamp lower down.

In addition, a spare locomotive was always stationed at Marble Arch to arrange for emergency train reversals or other special requirements. The maximum service required 22 train sets, thus 25 locomotives out of the original 28 were required to be operational. Two of the locomotives were fitted with tramway-type trolley poles for yard shunting at Wood Lane depot.

The yard at Wood Lane was equipped with tramway type overhead wire to avoid the use of conductor rails where staff would be working and to enable rakes to be collected easily from the covered sheds. Originally, two steam locomotives had been acquired from Hunslet for installation work. Numbered 1 and 2, they were utilised for yard shunting and for collecting the coal wagons for feeding the power house. The electric locomotives with the trolley poles were also used on the power station sidings.

In addition to the experiments with the geared locomotives, four of the passenger cars (Nos 54, 81, 84 and 88) were converted into motor cars to test the newly invented Sprague-Thomson-Houston multiple-unit control system. This system had been invented by Sprague and first introduced in Chicago in 1898, enabling a number of separate motor cars in the same train to be controlled from a single master controller at the front without it being necessary to pass power lines along the train. The control was achieved by utilising a number of low-current electrical circuits operating remotely the control switches which made and broke the main power circuits.

The cars were fitted for experimental running by the provision of a false floor of about 18ft (5.486m) length above one new motor bogie of the McGuire cast-steel type carrying two GE73-type nose-suspended traction motors. The control equipment was placed on the gallery created by the false floor above the motor bogie and occupied the first two window bays of the car body. This was the first operational multiple-unit equipment installed in Europe.

The non-automatic electro-magnetic contactor control, with open circuit transition from series connection of the motors to the parallel connection, was installed by BTH to the design of General Electric (American) in accord-

*Below:*
**Inside the cab of a Central London locomotive showing the main controller and driving position. The control handle could be repositioned so the driver could face either way, but the Westinghouse brake valve and handbrake wheel remained fixed on one side.**

*Above:*
**A Central London locomotive at the head of a train of Gate stock outside Wood Lane depot. No current rails are in evidence and the overhead trolley wires for the shunting locomotive are just visible.**

*Below:*
**One of the motor cars supplied by the Metropolitan Amalgamated Railway Carriage & Wagon Co to replace the original Central London locomotives in 1903.**

ance with the Sprague patents. The control was achieved by utilising nine low-current electrical circuits which operated some 13 contactors remotely on each motor car to provide five series and five parallel notches in the accelerating sequence. The control jumpers carrying the nine car cables were situated under the car canopies. These converted motor coaches, which had eight seats in a two-by-two arrangement on the rear half of the gallery which housed the control gear, were formed up into two six-car trains for the experimental operation. The driving positions on the paired motor coaches were on opposite sides of the cab so in fact the driver was on the same side of the train whatever direction it travelled. This odd practice was adopted because this was the position occupied on the displaced locomotives. No deadman's feature was as yet provided and the secondman was carried in the cab, although no coupling up or uncoupling

was now required. The first of these motor coach trains entered experimental service in September 1901.

The tests with these trains proved conclusively the vastly superior performance of multiple-unit trains as far as vibration was concerned. There was the added bonus of the easier reversal at terminals with no coupling problems involving locomotives. Orders were therefore placed for 64 new motor cars and on delivery the converted experimental motor cars were renumbered 201 to 204. The delivery of new motor cars Nos 205-68 took place in the spring of 1903, being completed by June. Twenty-four (205-28) were supplied by the Metropolitan Amalgamated Railway Carriage & Wagon Co, and the other 40 by the Birmingham Railway Carriage & Wagon Co. The seating capacity of these cars was 42, 18 in longitudinal seats and 24 in three two-and-two transverse bays at the motor end of the passenger saloon.

The vehicles had a similar general appearance to the trailer cars but had a single driving end with upswept frames above the single motor bogie. This motor bogie had a 6ft (3.810m) wheelbase and carried two GE66-type traction motors. These motors were of General Electric (American) design and of simple construction with four main poles series-wound without interpoles and axle-hung with nose suspension — the way all traction motors on tube cars have been mounted since, except on experimental vehicles.

The third rail shoe making contact with the centre current rail was mounted on the motor frame and was rather large, but no shoe was provided on the trailer bogie.

The control compartment and driving cab were of steel and had an arch roof while the passenger section had a clerestory roof, being constructed mainly of wood. Two of the Birmingham cars however had all-steel bodies without the difference being apparent from their appearance. The control compartment occupied about 12ft (3.658m) of the total vehicle length.

Because the driving position had been determined by the practice adopted on the locomotives, the new motor cars were also provided with left-hand and right-hand running. The cars facing towards the Bank had the driving position on the right-hand side of the cab while cars facing Shepherd's Bush had the driving position on the left-hand side. The trains did not turn until after the opening of the Wood Lane extension loop in 1908. After the opening of this loop the designations 'A' and 'B' were used for west and east-facing motor cars respectively to avoid incorrect coupling when the cars faced the wrong way. Motor cars were then usually kept in pairs on six-car trains.

*Above:*
**The interior of a Central London motor car, circa 1908, with fixed arm rests and rattan seating and with route maps on the ceiling.** *LRT U45901*

*Below:*
**The movable platform at Wood Lane station which allowed access to the depot sidings from the platform. The platform was controlled from the signalbox adjacent to the location, and its movement was small as it required only a few inches to enable the corner to clear a train turning into the sidings from the platform.**

In 1904, 66 of the original trailer cars were converted to control trailers, but at the time retained their original numbers; and they were supplemented by an additional six steel control trailers from the Birmingham company.

It was intended originally to have three motor cars per train but the difficulty of providing a free passage through the equipment chamber caused the train formation to remain at six cars with a motor at each end. At the right-hand side of the motor bogie when in a leading position (left-hand side when trailing), the 'last car brush' was fitted. The normal formation was M-T-CT-CT-T-M, although some trains were made up with five trailers to make seven-car formations. The conversion to control trailer was made by adding a divided front bulkhead with two windows and filling the gap with a roller shutter instead of a swing door. The cabs of the control trailers still had gate sides. As no deadman's control was available until later, two men rode in each cab.

The first extension to the Central London Railway was opened on 14 May 1908 to serve the Franco-British Exhibition at White City and consisted of a sharply-curved loop. A single platform station was constructed on the loop at Wood Lane, which improved upon the terminal working at Shepherd's Bush, but of course it turned the trains each time they passed round the loop. One other feature of the White City Loop was that the trains traversed in an anti-clockwise direction in order to accommodate the existing connections to Wood Lane depot.

Between 1912 and 1914 the line was resignalled with ac track circuits controlling all electric signals, combined with electro-pneumatic train-stops. Prior to the introduction of this signalling there had been 14 signalboxes between Shepherd's Bush and the Bank. At three stations which were on split level, two boxes (one for each direction) had to be provided, namely Post Office (now St Pauls), Chancery Lane and Notting Hill Gate. The 'brush-on-last-bogie' system was employed to check the train had passed into a section, allowing the signalman to free the section in the rear for the next train. Thereafter, with tripcocks on the motor cars and control trailers and a deadman's handle fitted to the master controllers, one-man operation in the cab became the rule. Cabs at this time too were converted to the conventional left-hand driving position to ensure that signal sighting became standard, although many of the control trailers remained unconverted for many years.

On 1 January 1913 the Central London Railway came under the control of the Underground group but retained its separate identity until the formation of the London Passenger Transport Board in 1933.

After the extension to Liverpool Street from the Bank was opened on 28 July 1912, the motor cars at the rear of the train tended to derail on the scissors crossing. Certain adjustments were made to the track alignment as well as critical control of wheel flange wear, but until this was completed the trailing motor car was cut out between Liverpool Street and the Bank.

In 1916 only 172 cars (64 motors, 40 control trailers and 68 trailers) were required to maintain the service, and the remaining 48 trailers and control trailers were stored.

In 1913 the Great Western Railway began construction of the Ealing & Shepherd's Bush Railway, extending the Central London Railway from the terminus at Wood Lane to Ealing Broadway. The line was actually completed in 1917 but the operation of a passenger service was delayed by World War 1 until 3 August 1920. The connection between the Central London Railway at Wood Lane and the Ealing & Shepherd's Bush extension was affected through the anti-clockwise station loop so that 'wrong road' running for a short length of the track was necessary. To restore 'right road' working a flying junction was constructed just west of East Acton. This wrong road condition of the tracks still exists and White City station, the successor to Wood Lane, has the trains running west on the right-hand platform. In Wood Lane station itself the original single-loop platform was

retained but a triangular platform arrangement was provided to accommodate the extension tracks. Incorporated in this set-up was a movable platform controlled from the signalbox, adjacent to the junction, to clear the depot junction when it was necessary to gain access to the depot. This platform extension piece was normally in a position to accommodate passenger trains working the loop in the local service, but was moved to allow trains to enter or leave the depot. The movement was small, requiring the platform corner to clear the centre of the cars as they took the curve.

For the Ealing extensions, 24 new all-steel motor cars were obtained from the Brush Electrical Engineering Co. They were 47ft 9in (14.55m) saloon cars, with arch roofs over the whole length of the car and not just the equipment chamber, and were provided with centre as well as end swing doors instead of gates; they were in fact the first all-enclosed tube cars without end gates. The saloon had seats for 32, but only eight were in transverse, located behind the draught screen on the switch compartment side of the single centre swing door.

The traction control equipment was provided with automatic acceleration. As all the earlier motor cars had hand notching these new motor cars were virtually incompatible with the original motor cars. The electro-magnetic contactors were controlled by a current limit relay (later known as an accelerat-

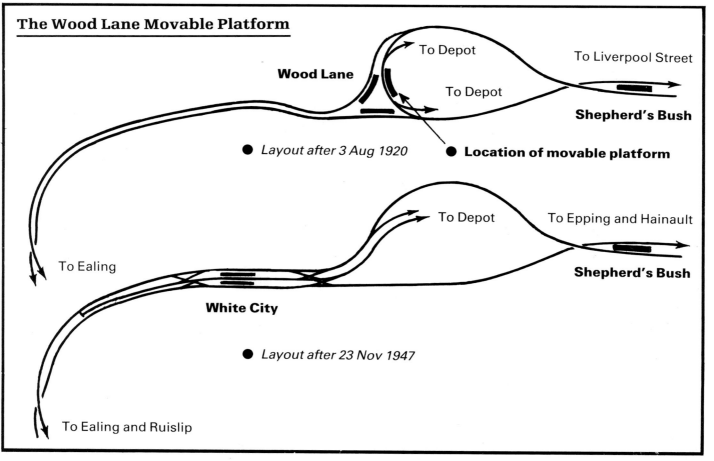

**The Wood Lane Movable Platform**

Wood Lane
To Depot
To Depot
To Liverpool Street
Shepherd's Bush

● *Layout after 3 Aug 1920*       ● **Location of movable platform**

To Ealing
To Depot
To Epping and Hainault
Shepherd's Bush
White City

● *Layout after 23 Nov 1947*

To Ealing and Ruislip

ing relay), which prevented the starting resistances from being cut out until the current taken by the traction motors had fallen to the correct level. It was the first use of this type of equipment on the Underground. The hand-notching by the driver was now limited to selection of shunting, series or parallel and did not require any manual stepping through the resistance notches. This improved multiple-unit system required the use of 10 control wires instead of nine. It is interesting to note that while hand-notching required a total of nine wires, only seven wires were in fact needed to provide the automatic accelerating control; nevertheless new 10-core cables and jumpers were installed on the new motor cars, and trailers which ran with them as extra wires were required to provide the heater control.

Trailer cars were modified to run with the new motor cars, and two separate groups of stock, known as Ealing stock and Tunnel stock, then existed on the Central London Railway. Normally the Tunnel stock (sometimes called the Local stock) did not operate beyond Wood Lane. The Ealing Broadway service was provided entirely by the Ealing stock which was equipped with the more powerful GE212-type motor instead of the GE66-type fitted to the original motor cars. As this was the first service of tube stock over open tracks, car heaters were provided on the new motor cars and on the trailer cars converted to run with them.

As the traffic on the Ealing section increased, the original provision of rolling stock was insufficient and eight of the Tunnel stock motor cars were converted in 1925/26 to augment the Ealing fleet. These were in fact reconstructed at Wood Lane depot, being equipped with the latest type of BTH automatic control equipment (to match that already fitted to the Ealing stock cars) and new G2-type motor bogies with GE212-type traction motors. These cars were subsequently known as the Yorke Converted cars after the engineer in charge of the project. At the same time a further eight trailer cars were converted to control trailers with totally enclosed cabs to match the additional motor cars, but no further alteration of trailer cars was undertaken at this time because the 1926 programme for reconstruction of the whole of the Central London rolling stock was underway. The eight original motor cars selected for the conversion were 205-06, 211-13, 220 and 226-27. After conversion they were renumbered in the series 293-300 in the order of their completion.

The Ealing stock motor cars had been delivered in 1915 and stored. In 1917, 22 of them, still lettered 'Central London', were lent to the Bakerloo for the Watford services because the rolling stock for this new service was

*Above:*
**A composite five-car train of an ex-Central London motor car at the leading end with ex-Piccadilly trailer cars, on the Watford extension.** *LRT U1966*

*Below:*
**The trailing end of a Central London motor car with the raised step for the guard, to provide a compromise height between main line and tube line platforms. The power cable from the motor car to the adjacent trailer can be seen at the bottom left.**

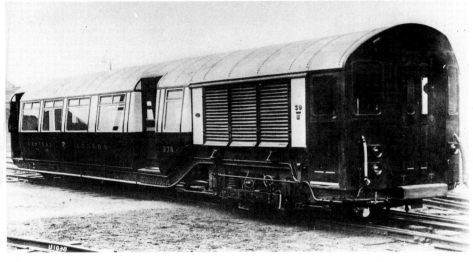

*Above:*

**A 1915 Brush motor car for the Central London Railway extension to Ealing Broadway, fitted with outside positive shoegear for running on the Bakerloo Line to Watford. The two-pole bus line box temporarily fitted for this duty can be seen under the solebar at the front.** *LRT U1038*

*Below:*

**A scene in the lifting shop at Acton Works under the 30-ton Duplex crane. On the hoist is the body of a Watford Joint stock motor car which has just been lifted from the works' accommodation bogies. Underneath, already placed on its own bogies, is a Central London Railway motor car of the type originally built in 1915 by Brush.** *LRT U4760*

not yet available due to World War 1. The Ealing motor cars had to be converted to four-rail working by making the equipment all-insulated and adding shoebeams and outside positive shoes to the motor bogie, with the addition of power lines and twin jumper receptacles. There was insufficient room for collector shoes on the trailer bogies of these motor cars, so the adjacent bogies on the Piccadilly trailer cars which had also been transferred to operate this service were provided with both positive and negative collector shoes. A power jumper was provided to connect these to the motor car. Dispensation had been given by the Board of Trade Railway Inspecting Officers for this to be arranged, because power line transfer from car to car on trains working in tube tunnels was allowed only on the Waterloo & City Railway. The Piccadilly trailer cars were made up into five-car blocks with a Central London motor car at each end.

The achievement of sustained high speeds up to 40mph on some of the longer sections out to Watford — with more than a mile between stops — caused weaknesses to become apparent in the equalising bar motor bogies. New

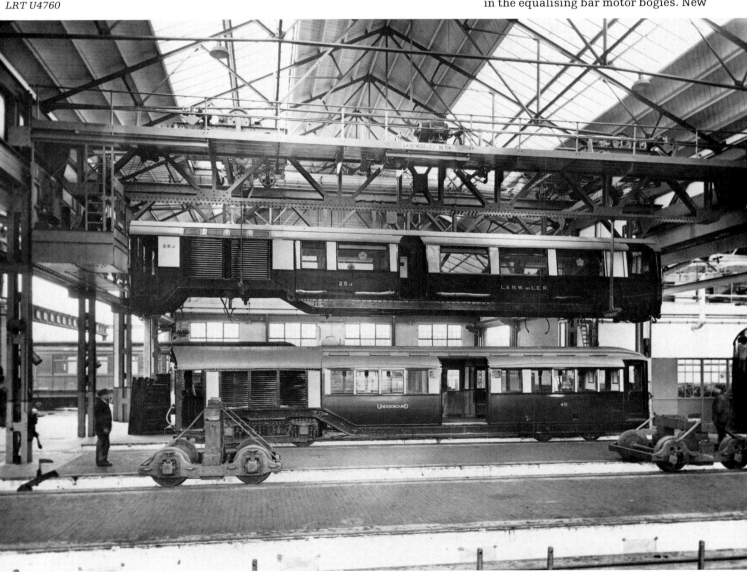

Type G motor bogies constructed of plate and angle by Cammell Laird were obtained to replace the equaliser bar type. These bogies were retained on the vehicles returned to the Central London Railway in 1920/21 when they reverted to the third-rail centre positive system for the Ealing service. During the time that the cars were withdrawn for the fitting of the new bogies, it was necessary for some of the ordinary gate stock trains to work to Watford.

Following the successful operation of pneumatically-operated doors on the Piccadilly and Hampstead lines, it was decided to rebuild the cars on the Central London for a further 10 years' service — incorporating the fitting of air-operated doors — because the smaller tunnel dimensions of the Cen-tral London Railway would not permit the introduction of the new air door stock being built for the other lines, without the expenditure of a considerable amount of money. The reconstruction of the existing stock was therefore considered to be the best solution. The Yerkes tube rolling stock had a length of approximately 50ft (15.24m) while the Central London rolling stock was only 45½ft (13.87m).

Premises were acquired in Feltham by the Union Construction Co, a subsidiary of the Underground group, for the express purpose of converting the Central London rolling stock. The work was undertaken between 1926 and 1928 when the whole fleet of 259 vehicles was transferred to and from these premises. The transfer itself was a major operation. The cars were worked from Wood Lane, the Central London depot to Ealing Broadway. At this location a crossover was used to transfer trains between the Central London Railway and the District Railway tracks to reach Acton Works. In those days however, the current collection systems on the two railways were different, so the Central London cars had to be hauled over the District Line tracks by steam locomotive between match wagons. These were special vehicles, usually open-type 10-ton wagons, with different couplers at either end for coupling between stocks with different arrangements. The cars were transferred to and from the premises at Feltham by Pickford traction engines hauling low-loaders.

*Above:*
**A scene at Acton Works about 1933 showing a Central London air-door converted train, together with a Hampstead train and a District train not fitted with electro-pneumatic brakes as they are not provided with the third receptacle box.** *LRT U12587*

*Below:*
**A rush-hour double seat as fitted on some end gangways of the reconstructed Central London cars after the fitting of air doors.** *LRT U5140*

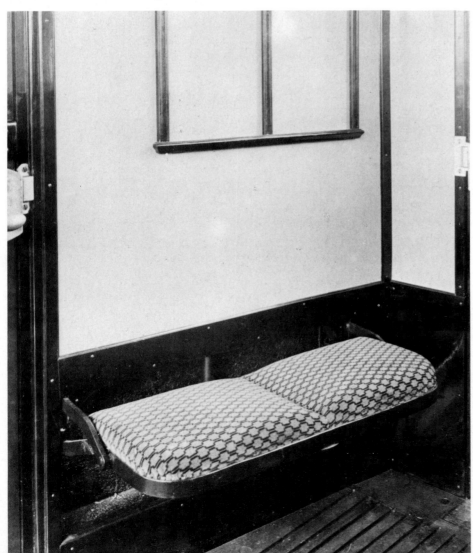

The trailer cars were rebuilt by removing the end bulkheads and completely enclosing the end platforms with an end door, and by adding four transverse seats; while two single sliding doors were inserted in the side of the cars. Similar treatment was given to the control trailer cars.

The motor cars were provided with one pair of twin sliding doors and the enclosed end platform at the trailing end became a guard's compartment.

The door control provided was different to that on other tube stock, being completely pneumatic and not electrically-activated. Two small air pipes, additional to those required for the Westinghouse brake, were taken along the train, one on each side. When these pipes were charged with air from the guard's door control valve to open the doors, they operated a pneumatic relay which connected the door operating engines to the brake reservoir pipe through a reducing valve. When the operating pipe was exhausted the doors closed. This arrangement proved to be too slow, with natural exhaustion of the air pipe, so an electrically-opened exhaust valve energised from a contact in the guard's valve was fitted to each car. The opening pipe was therefore only charged from one end — that which was connected to the guard's control valve — but exhausted for closing at several points. This system actually worked extremely well. The last Central London-type train operated in service on 13 July 1939.

In addition to the fitting of air doors, the cars were equipped with an emergency lighting and 'loudaphone' communication circuit fed from a 12V battery. No arrangements were made for Central London trains to be worked by more than two motor cars so that six-car trains became the rule.

# 4.  The Yerkes Tubes

The three tube lines which subsequently became known as the Bakerloo, the Piccadilly and the Hampstead were started in different ways by different people, but came under the influence of American financier Charles Tyson Yerkes before any operation took place. Although not physically connected in any way, these three lines were placed under one management on 1 July 1910 as the London Electric Railway. The combining of these three lines was the first of the groupings which finally resulted in the complete unification of the Underground system in London.

The Baker Street & Waterloo Railway was incorporated in 1893, construction beginning in 1898 under the auspices of the London & Globe Finance Corporation. Financial difficulties arose and Charles Tyson Yerkes acquired the property, transferring the construction to what in 1902 became the Underground Electric Railway of London Ltd.

On 10 March 1906 the line between Baker Street and Kennington Road (now Lambeth North) was opened. There was a station below the main line Waterloo station so the popular press dubbed the line the 'Bakerloo', and this appropriate name has been recognised and retained ever since.

The whole line was in tunnel except for the rolling stock depot, which was in an excavated area near St George's Circus, subsequently named London Road depot. Railway access to the depot was gained through a single bore tunnel approached from a trailing junction on the northbound road south of a scissors crossover immediately south of Kennington Road station (Lambeth North).

On 5 August 1906 the line was opened to Elephant & Castle station, while on 27 March 1907 the line was extended at the other end to a station then named Great Central, but shown on contemporary maps as Lisson Grove. The name originally proposed had been Marylebone, but the name Great Central had been used at the special request of Sir Sam Fay. Subsequently the line was extended on 15 June 1907 to Edgware Road, which remained the terminus of the Bakerloo Line for 6½ years.

The Great Northern, Piccadilly & Brompton Railway was the next to be opened to public service, over the whole route between Hammersmith and Finsbury Park on 5 December 1906, but the actual opening ceremony by the Rt Hon David Lloyd George, then President of the Board of Trade, actually took place on 15 December. There were 22 stations on this line in a length of 8¾ miles. Various intermediate stations were not completed, being opened subsequently:

*Below:*
**A Bakerloo motor car, the first one of the breed, outside the premises of the American Car & Foundry Co at Trafford Park. The bodywork is finished but the shoegear and electrical equipment is as yet unfitted.** *LRT U54036*

South Kensington on 8 January 1907, Down Street on 15 March 1907 and Covent Garden on 11 April 1907. In the course of time some of the original stations were closed or had their names changed. In 1932 Gillespie Road became the Arsenal in honour of the football team which brought plenty of traffic to the railway. At the same time York Road was closed; and Down Street too was closed in 1932. Dover Street was rebuilt and renamed Green Park in 1933 and finally Brompton Road was closed in 1934.

The Holborn-Strand (Aldwych) branch — a third of a mile long with double track — was opened on 30 November 1907. The development of this section of line arose from the antecedents of the amalgamation of two schemes, the Brompton & Piccadilly Circus Railway and the Great Northern & Strand Railway, by the financial interests of Charles Tyson Yerkes in 1901. After a complicated financial struggle the scheme promoted ensured the construction of the railway between Finsbury Park and Hammersmith, but included the small appendage to the Strand.

The Piccadilly Line as built emerged from the tube tunnels for the last half-mile to Barons Court and Hammersmith station, a section of track which was shared with the Metropolitan District Railway. As originally built the

*Below:*
**Map showing the extent of the tube railways exploited by the Yerkes group, which eventually came together in 1910 as one railway under the title of London Electric Railway.**

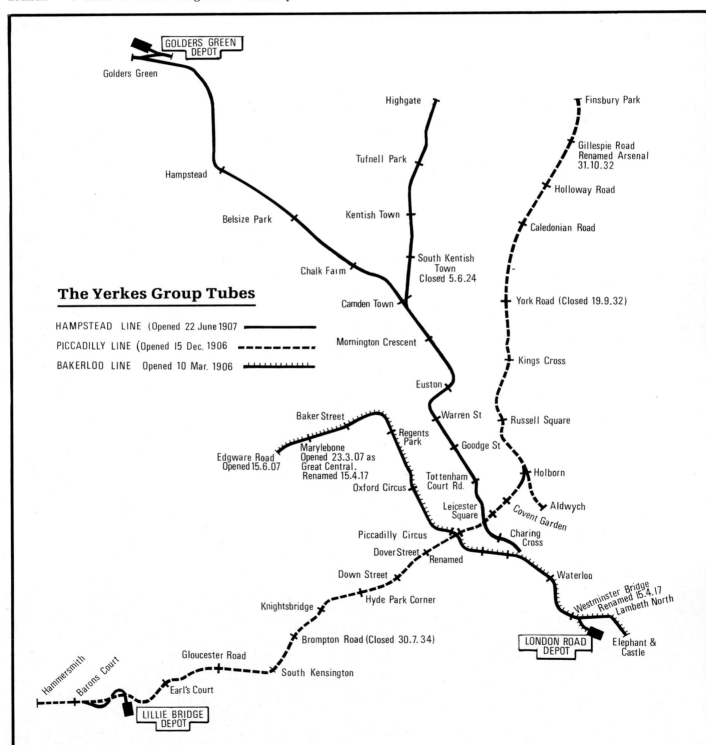

## The Yerkes Group Tubes

HAMPSTEAD LINE (Opened 22 June 1907) ——————

PICCADILLY LINE (Opened 15 Dec. 1906) ----------

BAKERLOO LINE Opened 10 Mar. 1906 +++++++++++

two most northerly tracks of the four were used by the Piccadilly Line trains into a two-track terminus at Hammersmith.

The sheds at Lillie Bridge, which had been used for the District Railway steam rolling stock, were modified to accommodate the Piccadilly Line rolling stock. Following electrification, the maintenance depot for the Metropolitan District Railway rolling stock had been transferred to a newly constructed depot at Mill Hill Park later renamed Ealing Common depot.

The Piccadilly trains reached their depot at Lillie Bridge by a connection just east of West Kensington station. To reach this connection, Piccadilly trains had to cross to the District Railway tracks east of Barons Court where a new four-platform station had been constructed. A vestige of this depot working remained for many years because a number of trains continued to be stabled at Lillie Bridge after the Piccadilly Line had been extended westwards. Until World War 2 the first Piccadilly train in the morning in a westward direction started at West Kensington station long after stabling of Piccadilly trains at Lillie Bridge depot had ceased.

The Charing Cross, Euston & Hampstead Railway was incorporated in 1893 with the intention of building a tube railway from Charing Cross to Hampstead with the possibility of a branch to Euston. These proposals (including the Enabling Acts of Parliament) were the first of the tube line proposals to come under the financial control of Charles Tyson Yerkes but were in fact the last to be constructed. The line from Charing Cross to Golders Green, with a branch to Highgate from Camden Town, was formally opened by the Rt Hon David Lloyd George, President of the Board of Trade. (The Ministry of Transport was not formed until 23 September 1919, and the powers of supervision of the railways until this time came under the control of the Board of Trade.) There were originally 16 stations, only one of which has since been closed, although a number have had their names changed. There was, however, one 'ghost' station, subsequently known as Bull & Bush because the surface station which was never constructed would have been adjacent to the licensed premises on Hampstead Heath. The platform level was in fact constructed but the top station and access passages and shafts were not.

The whole of the Hampstead Line was in tunnel except for the short

*Above:*
**The interior of an original American Car & Foundry Co car for the Bakerloo before the final preparation for service. Lighting fittings are not in place and no route diagrams or adverts have been fixed.** *LRT U54034*

*Below:*
**A Hungarian-built motor car for the Piccadilly Line. The plug-type tripcock and hose connection are plainly visible at the leading end of the motor bogie.** *LRT U1045*

*Top:*
**The interior of a Piccadilly motor car before the fitting of arm rests between the side seats, looking towards the driving end.** *LRT O22996*

*Above:*
**One of the seven Hungarian-built control trailers which was rebuilt at Golders Green depot to become a motor car for operation on the Bakerloo. The original gate trailing end was retained but a centre swing door with electric door lock was added in the reconstruction.** *LRT H/9420*

approach to Golders Green, the terminal station, and where the rolling stock depot was located. The main route was 5½ miles long and the branch 2½ miles, so that the whole railway had a total route length of eight miles. The junction was south of Camden Town where a four-platform station had been constructed. The depot was situated on the southbound side of the main tracks at Golders Green, at this time only a two-road terminal.

All three of the Yerkes tubes were constructed to the same specification, with a good alignment, a standard completed diameter of 11ft 8½in and transition curves sufficiently wide to allow the use of longer and wider cars than the earlier tube lines.

Although all the three lines were not physically connected — or, for that matter (with the exception of the Piccadilly), were not connected in any way with any other railway — the general design of the rolling stock obtained was similar. Three different car builders were involved but the coupling and operation of all the cars was compatible. It was at this time that the word 'cars' was used for Under-

ground passenger rolling stock in preference to 'carriages', because of the American influence and 'trucks' was used to describe the 'bogies' of these cars.

The American Car & Foundry Co of America built 108 cars for the Bakerloo and 150 cars for the Hampstead. The car builders acquired premises in Trafford Park, Manchester, to carry out the finishing and equipping of the cars. The electrical equipment was manufactured in England by BTH to American General Electric design.

Half of the Piccadilly cars were built by the Hungarian Railway Carriage & Machinery Works at Raab in Hungary and half by Les Ateliers de Construction du Nord de la France of Blanc Misseron. The car bodies from Raab came by rail to Rotterdam for shipment to Tilbury. After delivery to the London docks the Piccadilly cars were completed in the railway workshop at Lillie Bridge.

The Bakerloo cars were transferred from Trafford Park to Camden (LNWR Railway Goods depot) in London, where the car bodies and the trucks were loaded separately on to low-loading road wagons. During the night these

were hauled by 14 horses to London Road depot where they were lowered down a specially constructed incline to rail level. A similar transfer was made to Golders Green depot with the Hampstead cars, but here the road wagons had to be taken up an incline to the railway tracks where gantry-type lifting tackle could be employed to put the completed cars on the track.

At the time it was alleged that the main reason for the purchase of foreign vehicles was the long delivery times quoted for similar vehicles built in England. After his death in 1905, Charles Tyson Yerkes was accused by the English car builders of double-dealing. Several concerns claimed that they had not been asked to tender, but it was counter-claimed that the production of a steel shell was outside the experience of the English car builders.

The original intention on all three lines was to operate six-car trains in the peak hours. The trains were to have a motor car at each end and centre trailers having a control position so that three-car trains could be operated in the off-peak hours. In order to achieve this arrangement, almost equal numbers of motor cars, control trailer cars and trailer cars were purchased. Subsequently, traffic did not materialise as anticipated and therefore a number of trailer cars became surplus to requirements for a number of years because only five-car and two-car trains were operated. In view of the fact that the lines were not physically connected, any interchange of rolling stock had to be arranged by road.

The cars were all just over 50ft (15.24m) long, 5ft (1.524m) longer than the Central London cars. The trailer cars had saloons on the underframe occupying 41ft (12.5m) in which 52 seats were provided, 16 transverse seats in the centre with the remainder longitudinal seats at each end, eight on each side being over the wheels of the trailer bogies.

The motor cars had trailing ends similar to the trailer cars but at the driving end had the frame upswept to accommodate the motor bogie. The 12ft (3.658m) control compartment (only 8ft (2.438m) wide and with straight sides) was above this, occupying the position of the two end windows of the trailer cars. The motor cars had a total of 42 seats with the trailing ends the same as the trailer cars, but had a third set of transverse seats at the motor end next to the control compartment. On the Bakerloo motor cars, provision was made for a further four transverse seats on the raised floor above the motor bogie because the switch compartment was only 8ft (2.438m) long instead of the 12ft (3.658m) provided in the later motor cars for the Hampstead and Piccadilly Lines. These seats were reached by a short stairway with handrails from the floor of the main

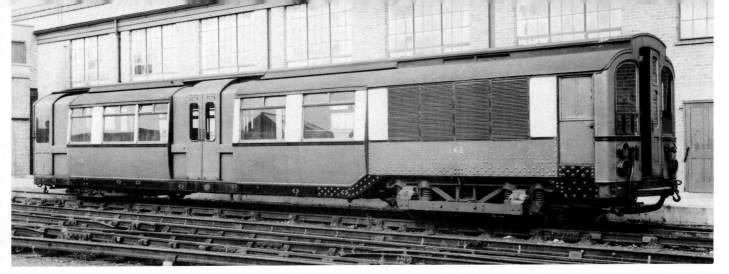

saloon, but were actually removed in 1913.

The car bodies had a 3ft 10in (1.168m) platform at the trailing end which was protected by hand-operated gates; at the ends of the passenger compartments were twin sliding doors with glazed panels leading to the end of the platforms. The swing gates were lever-operated by a single gateman straddling the ends of adjacent cars.

The motor bogies had cast steel frames with a wheelbase of 6ft 6in (1.981m) and 36in (914mm) diameter wheels. The bogie frame was suspended from each axle box by a pair of coil springs one on each side of the axle box. Two GE69 non-interpole, totally-enclosed, nose-suspended motors were fitted to the bogies using a gear ratio of 3.37. These motors were four-pole machines and, although of an improved pattern, were still vulnerable to heavy starting currents and thus failures were frequent. Traction motors of this type required rewinding and extensive repairs every three years on average.

The trailing bogies had a 5ft (1.524m) wheelbase and 38in (965mm) diameter wheels, being low-slung to allow accommodation under the low floors of the car bodies, which were only 1ft 10in above the rail level.

The traction motors and the electrical equipment were supplied by BTH to the American Sprague-Thomson-Houston multiple-unit system using electro-magnetic contactor gear but incorporating the improvements which had developed since the Central London installations a few years earlier. The improvements to the electrical system included 'bridge' transition for reconnecting the two traction motors on each motor car from series to parallel and the provision of a deadman's handle on the master controller. The introduction of bridge transition when changing the connections of the motors avoided the kick which gave an unpleasant sensation to passengers when the older open-circuit transition was used. This control circuit change not only improved the comfort of the passengers but also the life-cycle of the traction motors.

The cutting out of the starting resistances was not automatic: the motorman had to move the controller through 12 notches by hand, and if this was carried out too quickly the carbon circuit breakers tripped out. Ten control wires were now required to operate the multiple-unit equipment, being carried through the train by means of a 10-wire jumper which was hung between the end bulkheads of adjacent car bodies and taken under the clerestory canopies which extended over the end platform.

A jumper for the lighting wiring was also carried in the same way. The main lighting was supplied from the traction supply at 600V with five 120V lamps fed in series in each lighting circuit. Two main circuits were provided and fed from each motor car, so that on current rail gaps only half the lights in each car were extinguished. When short trains with a control trailer were operated, a shorting plug had to be used to connect the two circuits together so that all lights were fed from the one motor car. On short trains, therefore, all the lights went out over gaps. Battery-fed emergency lights, which came on when the traction-fed lights failed, were not fitted until 1914.

As originally constructed the lines were not provided with working loops: the cars were all left- or right-handed and the car ends were therefore designated 'A' or 'B'. Automatic mechanical couplers designed by an American engineer named Ward (who, as the Rolling Stock Engineer, was among the team provided by Yerkes) were provided for coupling the cars. This design avoided the necessity for the shunter to get between the cars during the coupling movement, although for uncoupling it was necessary for the equipment to be unlatched by the shunter's pole. The Ward coupler

*Top:*
**The Hungarian-built Gate stock motor which in 1911 was used for an unsatisfactory trial of pneumatic doors. The doors, which were fitted on the outside of the car body, were subsequently modified to be mechanically operated by capstan and wires controlled by the conductor or guard. The car was later used as the Aldwych shuttle car until 1930, having a master controller fitted on the end gangway.** *LRT U7207*

*Below:*
**A Hampstead motor car and trailer car. The destination plate was required from the beginning on this line as there were a number of different destinations. The orientation plate, on this car showing the letter 'A', was required only after the opening of the Charing Cross loop in 1914. The numeral '10' is the train working number.** *LRT U34522*

became the standard for Underground trains in London for many years, and although it has now been superseded it is still used for a number of special duties.

Above the 'B' end coupler a centre spring-loaded buffer was provided and this mated with a solid buffer on the adjacent 'A' end of the adjoining car. Also provided were emergency side chains fixed to the ends of the body frames to prevent parting should the coupling break. In later years these chains were not coupled until required after the failure of the drawgear because it had been found that under conditions of coupler failure the resulting snatch often broke the emergency chains as well.

In addition, two air hoses were carried at waist level at the ends of the car bodies, one carrying the compressor or main line air supply and the other the Westinghouse air brake pipe which, if exhausted by being parted in an emergency, would cause the brakes to be applied immediately. The handing of the car ends simplified the provision of these two air connections because there was no room to carry these below the drawgear and therefore make them reversible. They could not be positioned above the central drawgear either, because this would have interfered with the doorway giving free passage through the train. The provision of a through gangway on tube rolling stock was required by the Board of Trade Inspecting Officers because of the confined space in the tunnels, necessitating the emergency detrainment of passengers through the train ends. The resultant handing of the motor cars to maintain the simplification of the coupling did not cause any difficulties in the early days as all the services were of shuttle type, so cars did not get turned. This simple situation was upset when on 6 April 1914 the Hampstead Line was extended from Charing Cross station (subsequently renamed Strand), round a single line loop with a platform below the District Line Charing Cross station. The passage of all the Hampstead Line trains round this loop turned all the 'A' and 'B' cars so that coupling difficulties then arose, and it was necessary to increase the spare rolling stock to compensate.

Electrical connections — that is the jumpers — were not provided at the front ends of the motor cars because in passenger service they were always at the end of the train. There was no rear lamp bracket to hold a tail lamp but a hole in the front bulkhead filled with red glass enabled the driver's oil lamp to shine through the red glass to act as the tail light.

Leather straps for standees were provided on a wooden rail suspended from the lower edges of the clerestory roof. Advertisement frames were also fixed at appropriate positions on the car interior, and route diagrams were

**Comparison of the gate ends of trailer cars of the Yerkes tube lines and the Central London Railway.**

*Above:*
**London Electric tube trailer car gate end.**

*Below:*
**Central London Railway gate end.**

fitted to panels across the car. Rattan was used for the seating, and smoking was permitted in the motor cars, which were provided with 'smoking' labels stuck on some of the windows.

The operation of these trains of Gate stock (as they became known) generally required one man for each car: on the leading car the motorman and on the last car the guard, with gatemen on the intermediate cars. The gatemen were required to open the twin sliding end doors of the car saloons as well as the swing gates on the platforms. The motorman was not provided with an assistant because the deadman's handle had always been provided, and the signalling system incorporated the use of tripcocks. A system of automatic signalling controlled by track circuits had been adopted by the Yerkes tubes. This was similar to that already working successfully on the Metropolitan District Railway after electrification, which had been developed in 1900 on the Boston Elevated Railway. The feature of the electro-pneumatic signalling system was the use of signals and train-stops actuated by the passage of the trains, so that signalmen were not required except at junctions and regulating points. The running rails were divided into track circuits which detected the presence of the train so that a normal clear signal was produced if a train was not occupying the track and only showed danger when the track was occupied. When a signal was at danger an associated train-stop was raised which made contact with the tripcock carried on the motor cars of the train (and also the control trailers), which automatically applied the brakes should the train pass the signal.

The signalling system installed in London included the use of illuminated diagrams in the small number of signalboxes provided. The first signal-box in the world with an illuminated diagram had been installed in the associated District Railway on 5 July 1905 at Mill Hill Park (subsequently renamed Acton Town). This arrangement was applied to signalboxes required on the Yerkes tube lines; the most important in the early days (apart from the terminals and depot access) was the Camden Town junction signal cabin.

A single-stroke bell was provided on each car platform, operated from the other platform. To start the train a series of signals from the guard at the rear to the motorman at the front was passed up the train from gateman to gateman.

Because very few six-car trains were operated there was a large number of trailer cars surplus to requirements, so some of these were transferred subsequently to the Bakerloo to provide the additional trains required for the extensions. It was not until after the end of World War 1 that six-car trains began to be operated regularly.

On the Hampstead Line, five-car peak-hour trains were usual. The original 60 motor cars and 90 trailers (of which only 50 were control trailers) provided 30 five-car trains of which 10 were block or indivisible trains. It was therefore necessary to convert 10 trailers to control trailers so that all 30 trains could uncouple. An increase in service was required and, by 1918, additional five-car trains were being operated, by the transfer of surplus Piccadilly cars to the Hampstead Line. A total of 180 cars of Gate stock were

*Below:*
**The end gates of the Yerkes tube cars.** *LRT 4809*

finally allocated to the Hampstead Line by the permanent transfer of five Piccadilly motor cars and 26 trailer cars. One Hampstead car (No 194) had been transferred to Ealing Common depot for modification to see if the American Car & Foundry cars were suitable for conversion to a centre-door arrangement.

The Yerkes tubes, being associated with the already-electrified Metropolitan District Railway, adopted the same four-rail or insulated return system of electrification, which had been used mainly to avoid the effects of earth leakage currents damaging nearby gas, water and telephone mains. With this system it was possible to avoid the stringent regulations limiting the voltage drop in the earthed rail required on tube railways. The American engineers associated with Yerkes were very familiar with this problem and associated expensive litigation on tramway installations in the USA.

These new tube lines reaped an added benefit from the adoption of the four-rail systems as a complete safety automatic signalling controlled by dc track circuits could be installed.

Using a two-rail current collection system made it necessary for the rolling stock to be fitted with additional shoegear to provide the negative pick-up. This arrangement is still standard on the London Underground.

*Above:*

**A number of Gate stock cars built in the period 1906-08 were released for works train duties after their useful passenger-carrying life ended. These cars in their turn were replaced by pre-1938 Tube stock, but one Hungarian-built car (ex-Piccadilly Line) was retained for preservation, it being proposed to restore it to its original condition when finances were available. The cost of such a restoration proved to be too high but the actual gate end of the car body was restored for exhibition purposes by Acton Works apprentices. This restored end is now one of the exhibits at the LRT Museum at Covent Garden.**

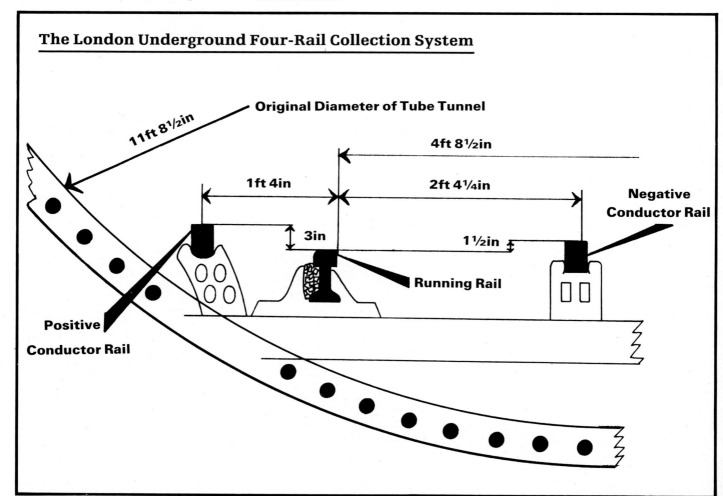

## The London Underground Four-Rail Collection System

Original Diameter of Tube Tunnel

11ft 8½in

4ft 8½in

1ft 4in

2ft 4¼in

3in

1½in

Negative Conductor Rail

Running Rail

Positive Conductor Rail

# 5.   Tube Extensions – Bakerloo 1914/22

After 6½ years with Edgware Road as its most northern terminus, the Bakerloo was extended on 1 December 1913 to Paddington where a scissors crossing was provided beyond the station for reversing the trains. The line reached Kilburn Park by 31 January 1915 and Queens Park on 1 February of the same year. The tube tunnels came to the surface to make a physical connection with the London & North Western Railway so that by 10 May 1915 Bakerloo trains began working over the main line to Willesden Junction.

After extended trials, which first took place in November 1916, tube services on weekdays only were extended all the way to Watford on 16 April 1917. Sunday services commenced on 6 July 1919.

In order to meet these services, additional rolling stock was required by the Bakerloo. Additional trains were first obtained by transferring some of the surplus trailer cars from the Piccadilly Line to run with 12 new motor cars, two obtained from Leeds Forge (Nos 38-39) and 10 from Brush of Loughborough Nos (40-49). Two new trailers too were obtained from Leeds

Forge. These motor cars introduced a number of new features to tube rolling stock including the provision of centre doors to the passenger saloon, although the end platform gates were retained. The provision of these centre doors, which were manually controlled, followed an experiment carried out on Hampstead trailer car No 1550.

The centre door swung inwards and was provided with a self-closing spring against which the passenger opened the door by hand. On the first cars with this arrangement, two doors were provided with rubber edging so that fingers were not trapped when the doors closed under the control of the hydraulically-damped spring. The twin swinging doors were not satisfactory because each single leaf was too narrow for a person of large bulk and tended to trap clothing against the other door if this remained closed, thus the provision of a single door became the arrangement. The most noticeable feature of these doors was that they were set back in the car side to gain additional headroom but not inset so far that it was possible for a passenger to stand on the outside with the door closed. Each pair of twin

doors was replaced by a two-window single door 2ft 2in (660mm) wide with a one window panel to fill the rest of the space originally provided for the two doors. There was sufficient space behind this panel for one person to stand without causing too much obstruction.

When closed the doors were electrically locked, and when this lock was fully home, a green light indication was given to the gateman on the end platform of the car. The action of the gateman opening the end gates caused the operation of a switch which released the middle door lock, allowing it to be opened by a passenger by pushing or pulling if he was outside or inside the car. A red light appeared on the conductor's platform when the door lock was withdrawn. In addition, two switches were provided on the end canopy for each side: one made sure the door remained locked even if the end gates were opened and the other allowed the middle door to be opened by the passengers even if the end gates were not opened. If the door was not properly closed the red light remained illuminated. The signal bell to the driver was given by means of a flexible wire in a tube the full length of the car. The one-stroke bell signal was passed from car to car by each conductor in turn and finally on the leading car to the driver.

These centre doors were not opened on the Bakerloo Line at Waterloo, Piccadilly or Paddington because of the curvature of the platform.

An emergency lighting system was also fitted to these cars: using a 12V battery, it illuminated three ceiling-mounted bulbs by means of a relay, which operated if the main traction supply lighting failed. Conversion of the older gate stock to provide battery-fed emergency lighting began with the introduction of these cars. Also now provided were electric tail lamps powered in an emergency by the battery supply. Nevertheless, a rear end collision at Warwick Avenue on 25 February 1918 caused the Board of Trade Inspector to suggest that reliance should not be made on electric tail lamps and the

*Below:*
**A 1914 motor car, built by Leeds Forge, at London Road depot. These were the first tube cars with middle doors, although the doors were not yet air-operated.**
*LRT U56960*

# Bakerloo Line Rolling Stock Transfers

Transfer route for *BAKERLOO* rolling stock between ACTON WORKS and the Line Depot at London Road before extension from **Baker Street** to **Finchley Road**

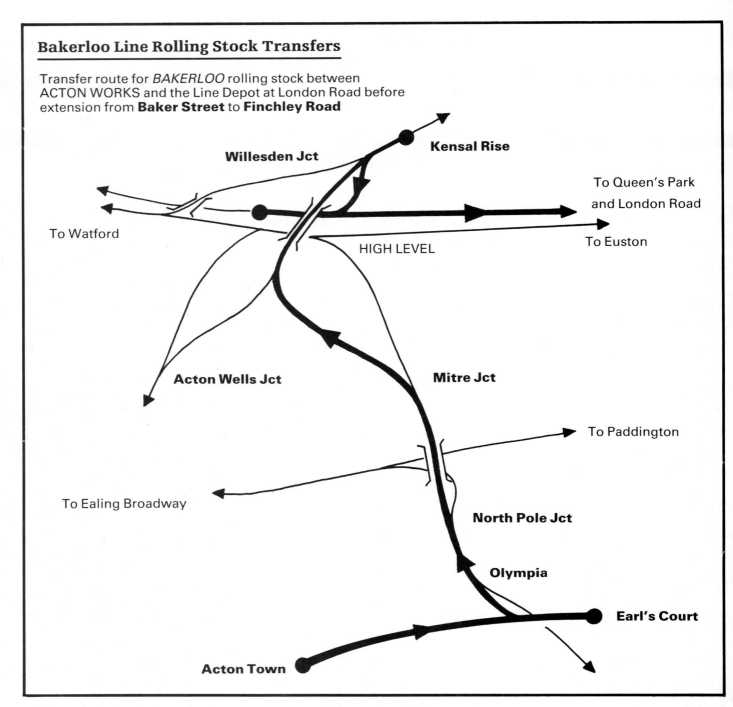

*Above:*
**The transfer route for Bakerloo rolling stock between Acton Works and the line depot at London Road, before the extension from Baker Street to Finchley Road.**

trains must continue to carry an oil tail lamp.

The motor bogie was constructed of pressed steel frames riveted together instead of cast steel as in the earlier Gate stock, and was equipped with two Type GE212 traction motors. For the first time on tube stock, traction motors with interpoles (sometimes called commutating poles) were provided. These motors provided a fundamental improvement in reliability by reducing the excessive sparking and commutation wear experienced with earlier designs, thus extending the maintenance periods, and they were a major step forward in the design of dc traction motors. The motor bogies were J-type, while the P-type trailer bogies were actually built by the London Electric Railway itself.

An additional safety feature provided at this time was the control governor, a pneumatically-operated switch which interrupted the control circuit in the forward direction if insufficient compressed air was available in the Westinghouse brake pipe to provide adequate brake power.

The motor cars were provided with 36 seats of which 16 only were transverse. Moquette trimming was used and armrests were provided on the longitudinal seats. So-called 'hygienic' enamel inserts were fitted to the standing passengers' handgrip straps mounted on a wooden rail.

In addition to these 12 new motor cars, seven more motor cars were provided by the conversion of Hungarian-built control trailers cars released from the Piccadilly Line. This conversion was carried out at Golders Green depot, to and from which the cars had to be transferred by road. The body and frame containing the end platform and the two end windows were cut away and a raised 'motor bogie' section spliced on to the frame. A swing door 2ft 2in (660mm) wide with locking arrangements similar to those fitted to the new motor cars was fitted on each side.

The seating arrangement consisted of two sets of transverse seats for 16 passengers on the motor end side of the centre doorway and longitudinal seats for 18 at the trailing end of the car. The original rattan seating was retained. The new J-type motor bogie was identical with those fitted to the new motor cars and was equipped with two GE212 traction motors. The original O-type built-up girdle frame trailer bogies were retained at the trailing end of these cars.

The Central London Railway had ordered 24 new motor coaches from Brush to provide rolling stock for the extension from Wood Lane to Ealing Broadway. These vehicles were delivered in 1915 but there was no railway for them to operate upon. Twenty-two of these cars were therefore loaned to the Bakerloo to provide trains for working the Watford service.

As explained in Chapter 3, these cars were the first all-enclosed tube cars not being provided with end platforms with gates, and also required modifications to be made for working on the Bakerloo system. The trains introduced to this Watford service were made up into permanent five-car sets in the formation M-T-T-T-M. The trailer cars concerned were mainly Piccadilly Gate stock including some control trailers. The end platforms on the Gate stock cars had also to be raised by fitting a false floor with a ramp from the passenger saloon to compensate for the higher platforms found at the main line stations on the Watford Line. The motor cars were not compensated in this way so that it was a considerable step down from the platforms to the passenger saloon.

The service to Watford was found to be particularly arduous for these motor cars. The equaliser type motor bogie with which they were equipped could not stand the strain of the higher speeds over fairly long distances between stations. During 1919 new G-type plate and angle bogies were fitted.

In 1914, rolling stock had been ordered from the Metropolitan Carriage, Wagon & Finance Co, a predecessor of Metropolitan Cammell Ltd, for the Watford service from the Bakerloo Line. This rolling stock was designed to the requirements of the London Electric Railway Co but was jointly owned with the London & North Western Railway. In fact a two-thirds share was held by the main line railway based on the relative mileage of the through service owned by the sharing companies. Unfortunately World War 1 intervened and the car builders were required to concentrate on armaments so that the service had to be opened with borrowed rolling stock.

However, delivery of the Watford Joint stock began in March 1920, consisting of 36 motor cars, 24 trailers and 12 control trailers, making up 12 six-car trains of the formation M-CT-M-T-T-M so that for the first time in an Underground tube train a motor car was provided in a middle position on the train.

Improved layout of the switch compartment enabled a through passage to be arranged for passengers in an emergency, and this allowed the provision of four-car trains for operation in the off-peak and for the full train to be operated with a motor car in the middle.

All the cars had bodies 50ft 10in (15.49m) long, about 1ft (305mm) longer than any cars so far provided for tube service. The car floors were 2ft 4in (711mm) from rail level (about 4½in (114mm) higher than tube train floors previously built) to help to provide a compromise between tube height platforms and those required for main line trains. When the Underground organisation had to arrange a similar compromise within its own operations when the Piccadilly shared the same stations with the District Railway, a compromise platform height was devised, so that the floor level on the Watford tube stock remained unique.

In addition to the extra floor height, larger diameter wheels were also provided in the interest of greater safety at the higher sustained speeds proposed: these were 42in (1.067m) for motor wheels instead of 36in (812mm), and 32in (914mm) for trailer wheels instead of 30in (762mm). The larger motor wheels enabled the higher speeds to be attained on the outer sections of the line by the same traction motor, the GE212 already developed for the new Central London and Bakerloo motor cars.

Over the motor bogie the Watford Joint Stock motor cars had the now conventional upswept frames which housed the control switch compartment. The BTH automatic accelerating multiple-unit control equipment incorporated in the recently-built Central London motor cars was installed. Speeds above 45mph were attained and in order to improve the riding quality the motor bogie wheelbase had been increased from 6ft to 7ft (1.829-2.134m). The motor cars seated 36 and the trailer cars 48, having two bays of transverse seats for a total of 16. Very little space was provided for standing passengers but amenities included small luggage racks.

Car lighting was by seven completely-enclosed opal glass bowl

*Below:*
**A Watford Joint stock motor car.** *LRT U944*

*Bottom:*
**A Watford Joint stock control trailer. The station non-stopping board is placed near the cab door.** *LRT U3370*

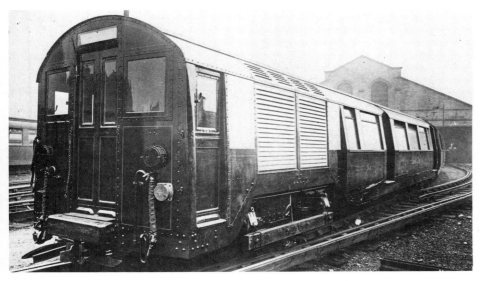

fittings distributed along the top of the ceiling and by a completely-enclosed bulb at the top of each window pillar. The bulbs were supplied from the traction supply at 600V with five bulbs in series. Two separate lighting circuits were arranged, one fed from the leading motor car and the other from the rear end motor car. Care had to be taken to ensure that the lighting switch was not closed on the middle motor car. Although there were 36 motor cars, 24 were facing north and 12 south, so that the middle motor cars were always north-facing motor cars. The control trailers were normally only used to convey the two cars from the uncoupling point to and from the depot and sidings and were not used in passenger service. No destination indicators were provided on these control trailers since they were not required to lead passenger trains.

A train heating circuit was provided, fed from the 600V traction supply, and these circuits had to be transferred to the trailer cars.

The motor cars were provided with illuminated roller blind destination indicators in what at the time was considered to be the logical place, above the train door. Previously, where destinations had been indicated, they had generally been provided by boards across and inside the non-driving window or externally across the top of the train door. As the Watford Joint stock hardly ever operated other than to Watford in the north and Elephant & Castle in the south the roller destination blinds did not get much use. It could be said therefore that the provision of roller destination blinds was an unnecessary luxury in advance of its time.

In addition to the head end destination signs, the sides of the cars adjacent to the doors were provided with non-stop indicators showing the stations at which the trains would pass. These indicators comprised 17 longitudinal slats hinged at the middle about the horizontal axis, blank on one side and with a station name on the other. The gatemen or conductor was required to turn these on the cars under his control to show the stations being passed. Actually there was a variation in the stopping points of the four trains per hour that operated through between Watford and Elephant & Castle so that some stations only had two trains per hour on this Watford service. The conductor was required to check the non-stop indicators on his cars at the commencement of each journey. It was normal for all Watford trains to pass Lambeth North, Regents Park and Maida Vale on the Bakerloo section and Kensal Green, Harlesden, Stonebridge Park and South Kenton on the main line. This latter station, in fact, was not constructed until 1917. These non-stopping trains therefore achieved speeds exceeding 50mph

*Above:*
**The interior of a Watford Joint stock trailer car. A total of 32 passengers were accommodated in the transverse seating arrangement.** *LRT U943*

*Below:*
**The swing centre door of the Watford stock with electric door-lock.** *LRT*

because there was nearly three miles between some of the stops. Although the cars were provided entirely with hinged doors — one in the centre and one at each trailing end — conductors were carried to ensure that each set of doors was locked before the departure of the train. The red and green light for checking the door position was provided to assist the conductors, but was very cumbersome as the time taken to load and unload passengers at busy stations was excessive. The development of a better door control system became desirable.

The standard tube stock coupling arrangement was continued: Ward mechanical couplers, spring buffers at one end and solid at the other, with the car ends handed to take electrical jumpers and compressed air hoses. The Westinghouse air brake system was employed, but because of the higher sustained speeds, clasp-type brake rigging was fitted to the trucks so that two cast iron brake shoes almost diametrically opposed were pressed on each wheel. The braking force was obtained at this time from one brake cylinder mounted on the underside of the car body of each car and transmitted to the bogies and brake blocks by means of rigging.

One feature which was not perpetuated in car designs after 1923 was the provision of leather-covered chains which were coupled across the car ends to give some protection against passengers falling between cars from station platforms.

The motor bogies were designated F-type and had 42in (1.067m) diameter wheels within a 7ft (2.134m) bogie wheelbase. This factor, combined with higher gearing associated with the GE212 motors (of which there were now six on a six-car train) meant that much higher speeds were possible. The trailer trucks had 36in (914mm) wheels and a 6ft (1.829m) wheelbase. For the first time on tube stock, trailer trucks were of plate and angle construction, being designated U-type.

These trains entered service during the summer of 1920, allowing the release of the borrowed Central London motor cars back to perform their original duties on the Ealing extension. Some of the trailer cars released from running with these cars were retained on the Bakerloo Line to enable the 25 five-car trains of Gate stock to be increased to six cars, while the balance were returned to the Piccadilly or Hampstead Lines.

# 6. The First Air Door Stock 1919/22

*Above:*
**A Cammell Laird trailer car. Note the jumper sockets for conveying control and auxiliary circuits along the train, almost at roof level.** *LRT U3366*

Following the end of World War 1 it became necessary to provide service improvements on the Yerkes tube lines. The Bakerloo improvements were achieved by the introduction of the Watford Joint stock but in addition an order was placed in 1919 with Cammell Laird & Co for 40 new cars composed of 20 trailers and 20 control trailers. These cars were the first tube cars designed to have air-operated doors and were fitted initially entirely with leatherette-upholstered longitudinal seats, 44 in each car. These cars were delivered to Lillie Bridge depot between November 1920 and August 1921 but they could not be used in passenger service until some Piccadilly Gate stock motor cars had been converted to run with them.

Twenty motor cars were eventually converted, two being completed in November 1920 by Cammell Laird, but the remaining 18, converted by Gloucester Carriage & Wagon Co, were spread over a further two years, the last one not being returned for service until June 1924.

While these new cars foreshadowed future developments in tube rolling stock they surprisingly included a number of features which were already obsolete. The trucks were of girdle frame construction with a 5ft (1.524m) wheelbase and one inside-hung brake block per wheel.

Four doors were provided down each car side: one was at each end of the car and the two in the middle were divided from each other by a thick pillar. Each centre door leaf was 2ft 9in (838mm) wide and slid into a pocket behind the seats. The single doors at each end were 2ft 3in (686mm), also sliding into door pockets behind the seating. The end communicating doors consisted of twin hand-operated sliding doors very similar in design to the end saloon doors of the Gate stock.

The sliding doors were vertical to within a few inches of the cant rail where they curved to become part of the roof line in order to provide an opening 6ft (1.829m) high from floor level.

Hand straps were not provided for standing passengers, the cars being furnished with grab rails instead. Horizontal rails were suspended from the roof and vertical rails were provided about 18in (457mm) inside the centre doorway on the edge of the draught screens.

The upholstery was known as imitation leather. The seat backs at the door pockets which protruded into the car were vertical, giving an uncomfortable seat in comparison with those clear of the door pockets.

The lighting was provided by twin fittings attached to the centre line of the roof with shallow open bowl type shades. The lighting circuits provided five lamps in series from the traction supply, as in the Gate stock trains. An emergency battery-fed lighting system was also provided.

The car ends had centre buffers and Ward couplers. The control and auxiliary jumper sockets were in the bulkhead near the car roof. In addition, leather-covered safety chains were fitted to help to fill the gap betwen vehicles.

The control trailers had an unglazed bulkhead with twin sliding doors (also unglazed) between the passenger saloon and the driving platform. The twin doors were latched back when the control trailer was in the middle of a train, allowing the driving cab to be a passenger vestibule. The driving controls were not secured in a cabinet but the main controls were inoperative without the insertion of the appropriate keys — except for the Westinghouse brake handle which could still be used to apply an emergency brake.

A special feature of all the cars was the provision of vertical oval windows on the end bulkheads, including the driver's look-out on the control trailer. As the cars were originally destined for the Piccadilly Line, destination boards were not provided as all the trains ran only between Finsbury Park and Hammersmith at the time.

To operate with these new cars, 20 of the 1906 Hungarian motor cars were reconstructed with air doors, having a new centre door as well as an air-operated door on the now enclosed end platform which replaced the gates. There were a number of detailed variations of the door arrangement because at this time consideration was being given to converting all the Gate stock to air doors.

Each door leaf was provided with an air engine using compressed air at the reduced pressure of 30lb/sq in. This air engine had two cylinders, one large and the other small. The arm which moved the door was fixed through a geared section to the small cylinder. When the door was closed, air pressure was supplied to both cylinders; to open the doors, an electrically-operated valve exhausted air from the large cylinder allowing the small cylinder to move in relation to the large cylinder and therefore move the door arm, thus opening the door leaf. De-energising this valve caused the compressed air to re-enter the large cylinder and close the doors. This arrangement also ensured that when no air was provided the door leaves could be pushed back by hand. This type of door engine was known as the B-type.

Originally each door leaf was fitted with a soft edge made of reinforced canvas. Inside this edge were placed electrical contacts which, when pressed together, interfered with the feed to the electrically-operated air valve working the engine. In this way, if someone became trapped in the door, it re-opened. This safety device was too sensitive, however, as it negated one of the main advantages of air-operated doors, the reduced station stop time. The system was discontinued after the first experimental period of operation. Nevertheless, this arrangement gave the name to the edging fitted to all modern air doors from whatever material it was made: the 'sensitive edge' in modern times has been made of some form of rubber and is no longer sensitive.

The door control system introduced in the 1920 Cammell Laird stock was designed to allow for two-guard oper-

*Top:*
**The interior of a Cammell Laird trailer car as originally built, with leather type upholstery and no arm rests. Note the shortened seats with upright back at the door pocket.**

*Above:*
**A close-up of a Cammell Laird doorway with a pilot lamp on the centre pillar.**
*LRT U1056*

ation of a six-car train or one-guard operation on a three-car train. The formation of the six-car air door train was M-T-CT-CT-T-M and the motor and control trailer cars were handed to provide 'A' and 'B' driving ends. Ten-core control jumpers were used to convey the traction control and door circuits through the train and these were connected from car to car at roof level. A short-circuiting plug had to be inserted at the front end of the control trailer when three-car trains were operated in order to complete the loop circuit for the door interlocks and also to connect the two independent 600V lighting circuits to obtain full lighting

with only one motor car providing the supply.

As both the guards, positioned on the motor cars on six-car trains, were placed on the trailing ends of the motor cars and controlled half the train, a jumper was provided in order to segregate their control to half the train. Later a switch was installed on the control trailer which when closed allowed it to be used as a normal trailer, avoiding the use of the jumper. The door control was normally arranged from the rear vestibule of each motor car, or from the non-driving vestibule of a control trailer car when operating in a three-car train set. The

*Top:*
**One of the French Gate stock motor cars converted to air-door operation to run with the Cammell Laird trailers.** *LRT U56957*

*Above:*
**The interior of a French motor car, looking towards the switch compartment, after its conversion for working the Aldwych shuttle service. Note the lamps without shades.** *LRT*

door control device consisted of a switch for normal electrical control of door operations and a pneumatic valve for the direct operation of the door at the guard's position when the guard was in place.

Each door had a mechanical door open indicator at cant rail level in the form of a yellow flapper arm which folded along the door when it was fully closed. By this device platform staff (as well as the conductors) were able to see which car still had doors unclosed. This arrangement was considered unreliable and removed in 1924, being replaced by interlock switches mounted on the door engines. Each interlock was activated by the door engine arm when the door reached its closed position. These interlocks were in a circuit which illuminated a signal lamp when all the doors were closed. The starting signal in the driver's cab was passed to the driver by the guard at the leading end of the train.

Another device fitted to the 1920 Cammell Laird cars, but not to the motor cars converted to run with them, was known as the door-closing plunger. This device was fitted on the centre door pillar on the outside so that platform staff could close the doors on that car by pressing it inwards. If the guard's door controller was still in the open position, pulling out the plunger would re-open the doors. This arrangement was removed when the cars were reconditioned in 1929.

Each door control position had on each side a door controller, a door opener, a switch box, a signal lamp and a lighting switch. The door opener was provided to enable the doors at terminals to be open while the guard changed ends without closing the doors. The door controller itself had four positions: 'off' — all doors closed but overridden by the door opener; 'running' — all doors closed; 'open local doors' — all other doors closed; and 'open all doors' — all train doors open. This controller was provided with two keys, one for unlocking and one for operating. Each train required two locking keys — one for each side — and one operating key which was moved from side to side. The locking key could only be removed when the operating key was in the off position but the operating key could be removed from the No 2 position of the controller to change sides.

The control trailers were provided with a mechanical bell cord similar to that provided in the Gate stock motor cars which could be used in an emergency when a guard was riding in the same car as the driver.

The converted motor cars were withdrawn from service in 1930, two being retained and further converted at Acton Works to make them suitable for working as single cars for the Aldwych shuttle service. Others were retained for use as ballast motor cars with engineering works trains.

The Cammell Laird trailers were originally numbered 800-19 and the control trailers 700-19. The converted motor cars were numbered 480-99. In about 1926 the control trailers were renumbered 1700-19 to clear the numbers 700-19 for new motor cars being built for the Hampstead Line. Subsequently the cars were renumbered again in 1930, the trailers being renumbered 1316-35 and the control trailers 2043-62. These numbers only lasted some four years as in 1934 there was a further renumbering of the trailers 7230-49 and the control trailers 5170-89 to conform to the London Transport renumbering scheme.

After the introduction of new stock on the Hampstead Line and the renovation of the Central London fleet, the Cammell Laird cars were considered to be drab and comparing unfavourably with them. Modernisation was therefore undertaken which consisted of the provision of one bay of transverse seats in the centre of each half of the car and the provision of armrests to the remaining longitudinal seats. The cement flooring was replaced by wooden slat flooring and the lighting arrangement was improved by fitting some swan-necked lighting fittings to the eaves.

In addition, the cars were formed into married pairs of trailer and control trailer with the coupling between the cars unchanged, but the outer end buffers and couplings were altered to marry with Ward couplers and spring buffers. The jumper sockets were removed from their central position to the conventional position on the solebars. The sliding train doors in the driving cabs of the control trailers were replaced by a normal swing train door. Door-closing plungers switches were added to the control trailer cab exteriors.

After modernisation and conversion the Cammell Laird cars were transferred to the Bakerloo Line where they were coupled to 1927 Metro Carriage & Wagon-built motor cars numbered 282-311 at this time. The transfer took place between January and October 1932, the main reason being that the Piccadilly Line was in the process of completing extensions involving considerable mileage in the open air. This stock was not designed for outdoor use, nor for high speed, and so the stock was very suitable for what was known as the Bakerloo Local service between Elephant and Queens Park. From Sept-

ember 1938 these cars were withdrawn from the Bakerloo Line and it was intended that some of the cars should be again reconditioned for a new lease of life for shuttle service on the Northern & City Line after it was connected to the Northern Line in the 1935/40 New Works Programme. The Local stock, including the Cammell Laird cars running on the Bakerloo Line, were the last purely Westinghouse-braked tube trains with the exception of the Aldwych shuttle cars.

Before the reconstruction work began, World War 2 intervened and the Cammell Laird cars were stored mainly at Cockfosters depot for the duration. Subsequently 35 of the cars were sold for scrap, while the five cars retained were converted at Hammersmith depot to form the Chief Mechanical Engin-

eer's instruction train. They were painted in a special livery of light brown with black lining and renumbered IC1075 to IC1079. No power cars were included and these cars, set up to demonstrate for instruction purposes all parts of equipment carried on Underground rolling stock, were moved from depot to depot by battery locomotives or ballast motors. The train was scrapped in 1968.

The two converted motor cars which became the Aldwych shuttle cars were originally numbered 481 and 498 and were renumbered 186 and 185 in 1927, but later in 1934 became Nos 3282 and 3283. The Aldwych Line, being single-tracked by this time, required only one train at a time to be in operation. Arrangements were made to change the cars over from time to time for maintenance purposes.

*Below:*
**A six-car train of four Cammell Laird trailer cars and two converted French motor cars on the Lillie Bridge depot shunting neck, which is now occupied by the Cromwell Road highway.** *LRT O24554*

*Bottom:*
**Aldwych shuttle car No 3283, converted from Piccadilly Line car No 498.** *LRT 24096*

# 7. The First of the Standard Stock 1923/25

In 1910 the Hampstead, the Bakerloo and the Piccadilly were amalgamated to form the London Electric Railway, consolidating all the tube lines at the time controlled by the Underground group. In 1913 the City & South London Railway also came under the control of the Underground group and plans were then made for this railway to be joined to the Hampstead Line which, together with additional extensions, eventually first became the Morden-Edgware Line and then the Northern Line.

The birth of the stock known for many years as Standard stock but which subsequently was designated pre-1938 Tube stock took place in 1923, arising from the need to provide additional trains on the Hampstead Line and, in effect, for the replacement of the original City & South London locomotive-hauled trains.

On 19 November 1923 the Hampstead Line was extended from Golders Green to Hendon and on 18 August to Edgware. The Camden Town-Euston connection and the enlargement of the City & South London Railway to Moorgate were brought into operation in June 1923.

New rolling stock was required for these new services and six sample cars were ordered from five different car builders to a standard specification, one of the main requirements being the provision of twin 4ft 6in (1.372m) air-worked doors on each side and seating for 48 passengers. Apart from the general specification the different car builders were given a free hand.

These sample cars were delivered to the Piccadilly Line, and a Press demonstration run with the cars coupled between two of the converted French motor cars took place on 3 February 1923. All these sample cars including the French motor cars were then delivered to the Hampstead Line by road and entered service in August 1923.

Each of the sample cars (all of which were trailers) had individual distinguishing features, not least being the interior finishings and colour schemes, although in outward appearance they were very similar. Two were constructed by the Gloucester Railway Carriage & Wagon Co (one being a control trailer) and one each was built by the Leeds Forge Co Ltd, the Metropolitan Carriage Wagon & Finance Co (known as Metro), the Birmingham Railway Carriage & Wagon Co and the Cammell Laird Co. The trailer cars were originally numbered 820-24 (later renumbered 7270-74) and the control trailer 720 (later 5271).

In 1923, orders were placed for 191 cars to be made up into five-car trains for the Edgware extension service and to replace the City & South London loco-hauled stock following the completion of the junction at Camden

*Below:*
**The front of a 1923 stock motor car as built, with destination blind above the front cab door, running number positioned near the roof and marker lights spread across the front.** *LRT L1191*

Town. In fact, 69 of these cars were owned by the City & South London Railway while the remainder were the property of the London Electric Railway Co.

This original order was shared by three car builders: Cammell Laird which built 41 motor cars and 40 trailers, Metro which built 40 motor cars and 35 control trailers, and Birmingham which built 35 trailers. All except two motor cars were equipped with Metropolitan-Vickers (MV) electromagnetic contactors arranged for automatic acceleration with bridge transition from series to parallel. The other two motor cars had General Electric Co (a British concern not related to the American GEC, whose British partner was the BTH company) equipment based on Swiss Oerlikon patents, but the arrangement also included electro-magnetic contactors with automatic acceleration and they were required to multiple with the MV equipment. This was the first time that bulk orders for electrical traction

equipment had been placed by the Underground group with other than the BTH company. It would seem that some contractual problems had arisen over the provision of equipment for the 1920 District Railway rolling stock (subsequently known as 'F' stock) which caused these contracts for tube train equipment to be placed elsewhere.

Subsequently orders were placed for a further 127 cars, which became known as the 1924 stock and consisted of 52 motor cars of which all but seven had GEC equipments. All were built by Metro. The Birmingham company built 50 trailers, while Cammell Laird provided 25 control trailers, some with MV and others with GEC equipment. This

batch of cars was provided to cover the extension to Morden, and because of this some 31 of the cars were owned by the City & South London Railway. At about this time too it had been decided to run some six-car trains instead of five-car ones and this prompted the ordering of more trailer cars than the actual balance for five-car trains required.

The motor cars were provided with driving cabs in front of the equipment compartment which was raised above the motor bogie by means of the usual upswept frame. The motor bogie was of a new robust plate and angle design, designated Y-type, with a 6ft 11in (2.108m) wheelbase and 40in (1.016m) wheels. The MV cars were equipped

originally with MV152 traction motors while the GEC cars had WT54 motors. The motors were in fact interchangeable although it was usual to keep them in pairs.

The passenger saloon of the motor cars seated 30 passengers with only eight in transverse seats and the remainder in longitudinal seats. In the early batch of cars the 5ft 11in (1.803m) doorway in the middle of the car side was provided with a centre pillar. Centre pillars were not provided in the trailer car doors, the overall opening being reduced to 4ft 6in (1.372m).

The rear vestibule of the motor car was arranged as a guard's compartment with hand-operated inward swinging doors. The guard's control was placed on the saloon partition because the access door when open covered the end bulkhead of the car, which in later stocks became the normal position for the door control boxes.

The door engine fitted to the doors on the 1923 stock was known as the C-type in which the arm operating the door was fixed to the moving small cylinder inside the large cylinder. The move-

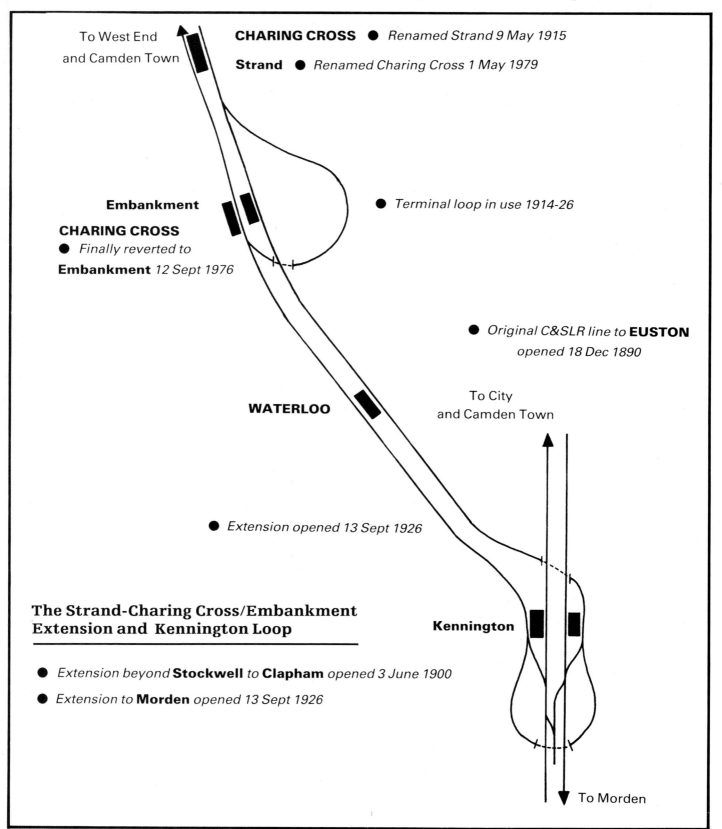

To West End and Camden Town

**CHARING CROSS** ● *Renamed Strand 9 May 1915*

**Strand** ● *Renamed Charing Cross 1 May 1979*

**Embankment**
**CHARING CROSS**
● *Finally reverted to*
**Embankment** *12 Sept 1976*

● *Terminal loop in use 1914-26*

● *Original C&SLR line to* **EUSTON**
*opened 18 Dec 1890*

**WATERLOO**

To City and Camden Town

● *Extension opened 13 Sept 1926*

**The Strand-Charing Cross/Embankment Extension and Kennington Loop**

**Kennington**

● *Extension beyond* **Stockwell** *to* **Clapham** *opened 3 June 1900*

● *Extension to* **Morden** *opened 13 Sept 1926*

To Morden

ment of the door arm produced an elliptical arc, and the arm was located at an angle of 22° to the horizontal when the door was open or closed. This had the effect of preventing the door slamming and getting it locked in dead centre, so that with air removed it was possible to move the door leaves.

This door engine was considered to be unsatisfactory and the 1924 stock introduced a new design which was designated the D-type: this type (with a minor modification altering the designation to DL) became the standard air door engine in all stock until 1931. In this engine the door arm quadrant was operated by a rack which moved in either direction by the balance between the large and small cylinders. Air was supplied to the large cylinder to close the doors; exhausting it caused the doors to open under the control of the small cylinder. This arrangement lasted until about 1934 when the introduction of new door circuitry and a new type of engine caused this system to be reversed so that air was exhausted from the large cylinder to close the doors.

In 1925 another 120 cars were ordered — 48 motor cars from Cammell Laird with GEC equipment and 67 control trailers and five trailers from Metro. They were required to provide increased train service with the opening of the Kennington Junction, both as to number of trains and the lengthening of trains from six to seven cars. At this time the uneven number of trailers and control trailers had caused the operation of some block trains containing only motor cars and trailers. This batch of 1925 stock helped to adjust the

position although Standard stock motor cars could be worked in the middle of trains, especially seven-car ones, so that the overall number of control trailers required was reduced.

The Hampstead Railway had normally operated five-car sets but when sufficient control trailers became available the formation became M-T-CT-CT-T-M. The familiar seven-car train formation did not appear until after 1926, although the design of the rolling stock would enable the trains to be made up into any formation within the platform and siding limits.

The Hampstead Railway introduced a loop working, with the extension from Strand to Charing Cross (now renamed

Embankment, with the old Strand station taking the name Charing Cross), opened on 6 April 1914, and the handed problems were then experienced. The new extensions however again included a reversing loop at Kennington for the Charing Cross Line, but in spite of this, when the Standard stock was delivered the practice of giving even numbers to 'A' end motor cars and odd numbers to 'B' motor cars was continued. This numbering system was also adopted for control trailer cars as well because these cars had to be handed also. Because of the operation of trains round the Kennington Loop, some stock became wrong way at times; to avoid difficulties of replacement in train formations, a turntable for single cars was installed at Golders Green depot where most of the running maintenance was carried out.

The 1923/24 cars could be easily distinguished from later stocks by the provision of vertical sliding windows which could be pulled down about 3in (76mm) for ventilation. These windows were fitted with a central brass knob near the top of the glass. Over the years these windows became a maintenance liability and later batches of stock were reconstructed with small drop ventilators windows, an arrangement which remained standard on all tube stock until 1960.

The trailer cars were just under 50ft (15.24m) in length and seated 48, with eight in transverse seats in the centre flanked by three longitudinal seats without arm-rests, although the longitudinal seats over the wheel arches had armrests. The control trailers were almost identical but had a driving cab

enclosure at one end, which reduced the seating to 44. In addition, the early batch of control trailers was provided with a guard's position in the driving cab; this was also fitted with swing doors. The trailer cars were provided with two pairs of sliding doors on each side without centre pillars or end doorways.

Until 1927, three men were still carried on a train: a rear guard who controlled the doors, a front conductor and a motorman. It was still the front conductor's job to give the starting signal to the driver of the train after receiving the 'all clear' signal from the rear guard. When the remote operation of the doors was achieved successfully, consideration was given to reducing the train crewing arrangements to two men. This was not completed until 1927 when train telephones were introduced that enabled guards and drivers to communicate. The main safety feature of the door system was achieved by

providing interlocks which were made when the doors were closed. Interlocks were also provided on the swing doors in the locked position, both at the guard's location and on the cab doors of the control trailers, but not on the cab doors of the motor cars.

As an additional safety measure, contacts were also provided in the signal circuit to ensure that it could only be completed if all the door-operating relays at all guards' positions were de-energised. When the circuit was completed the guard could see two pilot lamps illuminated. These lamps, mounted at roof level, were illuminated in parallel so that the 'doors closed' mode was not lost if one lamp had failed. Originally the starting bell was energised in the driver's cab by the operation of the signal bell at the leading guard's position. This arrangement had to be altered when the trains were manned only by two men, and at the same time the provision of a guard's position on control trailers was abandoned.

All the 1923/25 stock cars for many years were recognised by the fact that they were provided with marker lights having external location plates on either side of the centre communicating doorway. This feature was eliminated from about 1927 when the original roller destination blind was removed from the centre roof position to make way for a ventilation duct. The destination plates and marker light cabinet was then placed on the offside front.

---

*Left:*
**The first vehicles of the Standard stock were delivered by road to Golders Green depot. The bodies and bogies were delivered separately and the cars were lifted by prepared gantries to enable the bogies to be placed underneath.** *LRT 16118*

*Below left:*
**A Y-type motor bogie for a 1923 stock motor car at the unloading gantry at Golders Green, about to be set underneath a newly-delivered car body.** *LRT 16119*

*Below:*
**A four-car 1923 stock train at Hendon Central soon after the 1924 opening of the extension from Golders Green to Edgware.** *LRT U3016*

*Above:*
**A double doorway of a 1923 Tube stock trailer car built by the Birmingham Railway Carriage & Wagon Co. The emergency door opening cocks were fitted to the bottom of the windscreen. On later stocks these and the small grab rails were omitted.**
*LRT U2680*

This arrangement then remained in force until marker lights became redundant with the removal of signalmen and the introduction of centralised control.

The basic general safety provisions for air door operation introduced with the operation of the 1923/25 stock on the Hampstead Line required that:

(1) The guard's swing door must be locked when not in use and the locking mechanism connected into the door pilot light circuit.
(2) Some doors on each car must have means of opening and closing in an emergency, independent of the electrical control circuit.
(3) The door engine and operating arm must be so arranged that the door in the closed position was locked but one door of each pair must be capable of a limited opening not greater than 5in (127mm) from the closed position.
(4) The signal to start the train must not be possible until all the doors were in the closed position.

The guard was now provided with only one key, called the position switch key, to open up the guard's position for operation. A feature of this control was that the guard could open the doors at one position, close the switch to leave the doors open, remove his key and close the doors from another position.

Two 10-core control lines were passed down the trains, one on each side. One carried the traction control wires and the other the door and lighting control circuits. The Westinghouse brake system using two air lines was employed, one carrying the main supply coupling the compressors together and providing the air supply for the other requirements such as the door operation. Each car was provided with a single brake cylinder mounted on the car body, which applied the brakes to the wheels by means of mechanical rods and rigging. Each wheel was provided with brake shoes which, at this time, were of cast iron. The motor bogie had two brake blocks

per wheel while the trailer bogies had only one block per wheel.

A special feature of the braking system was the provision of an indicator light in the motorman's cab, which was illuminated when air entered the brake cylinder of the leading motor car. This was an early attempt to solve the problem of flat wheels caused by unreleased brakes. Unfortunately, this arrangement was found to be virtually ineffective as it did not deal with the source of the problem and in fact made matters worse.

The 1923 cars had safety chains which were provided between the car bodies but these were subsequently not used. Some of the cars retained them for their entire life although the idea of connecting chains between cars was not continued in London. The chains were replaced by fixed grab rails on subsequent stock.

When it became necessary to make up trains with motor cars in the middle, the problem of the 600V lighting circuits had to be solved as one circuit was fed from an 'A' motor car while the other circuit secured its power from the 'B' motor car. The train pipe isolating cock was provided with a mechanically-coupled switch which prevented that motor car — however handed — from feeding the appropriate lighting circuit. This switch was inoperative when the motor car was at the driving end of the train because the cock was in the isolating position. Subsequently a pneumatic switch which became known as the lighting governor replaced the mechanically-operated device. When pneumatically-charged this switch isolated the power feeds to either the 'A' or 'B' lighting circuits according to the type of car on which it was placed. A short-circuiting plug was inserted into the auxiliary 10-core jumper head of control trailer cars when two-car or three-car trains were operated so that the 'A' and 'B' lighting circuits were both lit from a single motor car.

Another pneumatically-operated interlock was provided to work with the main reservoir supply, this switch isolating the bell in the driver's cab and breaking the door interlock circuit so that the cars ahead of the switch were included in the safety circuit.

The provision of heaters was now considered necessary because the trains were running out of the tunnels at Golders Green and working on to Edgware. On early cars for the service the heaters provided had no through control, being switched on by key-operated switches almost at floor level on each car. These heaters were used only to preheat the trains, being switched on about half-an-hour before entering service and then subsequently cut out. Cars operating on the Hampstead Line later were not fitted with heaters as practically all the service was in tunnel.

# 8.  More Standard Stock 1926/27

At first it was intended that the Gate stock cars on all lines should be converted to air doors in a fashion similar to the Hungarian cars converted to run with the Cammell Laird cars and the sample Hampstead Line Gate stock trailer car. Car No 194, originally built by American Car & Foundry Co, was rebuilt at Ealing Common depot (it is believed) to air doors and renumbered 1550. Subsequently it was only the Central London cars that were in fact dealt with, partly because the restrictions of the tunnels required special consideration and partly because the new Standard stock on the Hampstead Line was obviously so superior that renovation rather than new-build would have been unsatisfactory.

It was therefore decided to replace the Gate stock on all three Yerkes lines over the next few years, beginning with the Hampstead Line. A total of 112 cars designated 1926 stock were obtained from Metro with GEC equipment, 64 being motor cars and 48 trailer cars, and a further 170 cars (63 motors and 107 trailers) with GEC equipment designated 1927 stock were produced. These cars were allocated to the Hampstead Line after delivery so that some additional trains could be operated and all trains raised to seven-car length. Ninety-one seven-car trains were required for daily service on the line, which subsequently became known as the Morden-Edgware Line.

Subsequently, a further 136 cars also designated 1927 stock, were built by Metro, but the 47 motor cars and 36 control trailers and all subsequent deliveries of Standard tube stock now had BTH equipment. In fact the BTH traction control equipment proved to be the most reliable and this concern or its successors supplied practically all tube stock traction control gear for over 35 years, except for a small number of experimental equipments. On the other hand the traction motors for all the Standard stock (except the MV cars) were provided by GEC. In fact, the MV and GEC equipments on the earlier cars were subsequently modified to take the BTH-type of interlocking equipment on the main contactors because this type proved more reliable. All the cars were compatible in that the equipments operated in multiple so that there was no segregation of the types. It was for this reason that they became known as Standard stock.

The MV and GEC 1923/25 motor cars were fitted with Y-type bogies and 40in (1.016m) motor wheels with MV152 and WT54 traction motors. The WT signified Witton, the main works of the (English) General Electric Co. These initials were chosen because the American-designed traction motors used the letters GE and these were supplied by the BTH company.

Most of the later Standard stock motor cars had a new type bogie, the Z-type with 36in (914mm) motor wheels fitted first to the 1927 stock.

The 'Z' bogie required a slight modification to the construction of the motor to allow for the nose suspension on the bogie, hence the motor was designated type WT54A. This type of motor became the standard on all subsequent rolling stock with 'Z' bogies. Electrically the motor was the same as the WT54 fitted to the 'Y' bogie. The compatibility between the motor cars with 40in (1.016m) wheels and those with 36in (914mm) wheels was achieved by arranging a different gear ratio. Those with 40in wheels had a gear ratio of 16:67 while the 36in had a gear ratio of 17:63.

Candle lamps were provided in each

*Below:*
**Hampstead Line Gate stock trailer car No 194, originally built by the American Car & Foundry Co, was converted circa 1925 as a prototype for the proposed conversion to air doors. This car was renumbered 1550 in 1926 and scrapped in 1930.** *LRT U57024*

car for use in emergency should the power be cut off, but subsequently installed in each motor car in addition was a 12V battery which fed an emergency lighting circuit, two or three small bulbs being placed in the car ceilings, together with a special lighting jumper which had to be connected separately from the two 10-core control and auxiliary jumpers.

Well advanced by this time were negotiations to reduce the train crews to two men because of the simplicity of control with air doors. One of the

*Above:*
**A Y-type motor bogie outside the rear of the lifting shop at Golders Green, where a traverser pit was provided to enable cars and bogies to be transferred from one road to another.** *LRT U4541*

*Below:*
**A 1926 'B' end (later a 'D' end) motor car with improved front design containing a marker light cabinet and destination box. The running number has now been transferred to the cab door.** *LRT U5010*

*Right:*
**The door control box and first type of 'loudaphone' installation at the guard's end for through communication with the driver.** *LRT U16465*

*Below right:*
**The interior of a 1926 Metropolitan-built trailer car which was the general pattern of all Standard stock cars.** *LRT U4951*

essential requirements for this change was the provision of a simple and versatile communication system between the motorman at the front of the train and the single guard at the rear. A 'loudaphone' system was adopted which used the same battery and train wires as those provided for the emergency lighting. After the trials it was arranged to retrofit the earlier stock. In addition the door interlock and bell circuit was modified to ensure that all the doors not in use — including the intermediate guards' doors — were properly closed before the signal to the driver could be given.

Seven-car train formations were then operated on the Hampstead Line and its extension (soon to be generally called the Morden-Edgware Line). Because there were still almost an even number of 'A' and 'B' end motor cars and control trailers, two different seven-car formations were made up — either M-T-CT-M-T-T-M or M-T-T-M-CT-T-M — and there were almost an equal number of each formation. On the Morden-Edgware Line it was convenient to detach three-car portions from the south end of trains at Morden and to detach the three-car portions from the north end at Edgware and Golders Green. The provision of these two formations was therefore suitable for this arrangement, provided the trains were the right way round at uncoupling time. The existence of the Kennington Loop, however, made the turning of trains inevitable and any disorganisation of the service could cause serious difficulties in the coupling and uncoupling procedure.

Although middle motor cars had been operated on the Watford trains for some years, the coupling and uncoupling arrangements on the Bakerloo Line were simple compared with those now required on the Morden-Edgware Line. A further modification was required to prevent the middle motor car of seven-car trains feeding the lighting circuit and thereby creating a through power bus line connection with the same hand motor car in the train, which would be very unsatisfactory when going over gaps.

To prevent the middle motor car feeding the traction motors on another car through the 600V lighting circuit, a lighting governor was provided (see Chapter 7).

When 'via Bank' and 'via Charing Cross' destinations were needed after the extensions to Kennington, the 1923/25 car driving ends were modified by the addition of a small white enamelled plate lettered 'VIA' just above the train door under the destination blind. Associated with this plate was a triangular 'board' rotating on a horizontal axis at the top of the train door. One of the faces of the board was blank while the other two carried BANK or CHARING CROSS for use as appropriate.

The 1926 stock cars had a new front design. The non-driving window sill was raised, below which a two-line rack for destination plates was arranged, one carrying the route and the top one the destination. In addition, a five-lamp marker light for destination codes was placed below the destination box, which now required plates and not a blind. Subsequently, the early motor cars were altered to match this arrangement, but the control trailers were not modified and carried the old marker light arrangements.

The heaters fitted to the earlier types of cars did not prove satisfactory in that a number of short circuits occurred, so they were removed and the subsequent batches for the Morden-Edgware Line were not provided with heaters.

The 1923/25 stock cars had also been fitted with V-type trailer bogies which had 32in (813mm) wheels, while later types of stock had a W2-type bogie which only required 30in (762mm) wheels. Thus, in addition to the motor wheels being larger on the earlier stocks, so were the trailer wheels.

Although the successful conversion of the Central London cars encouraged the preparation of plans to convert all the Gate stocks for operation on the Piccadilly and Bakerloo Lines, the improvements on the Hampstead Line with the new stock caused second thoughts. It was also found that the organisation set up at Feltham could in fact build cars of a simple construction almost as cheaply as the cost of conversion. The 1927 Metro-built cars with BTH equipment were used to replace the Piccadilly Gate stock but an order was placed with the Union Construction Co for 77 motor cars, 37 trailer cars and 68 control trailers which were required to make up six-car trains for the Bakerloo as well.

These cars had similar electrical equipment and door arrangements and could couple mechanically and electrically with all the modified Hampstead cars. The main difference was in their lighter construction. A Feltham-built motor car weighed under 29 tons, but a 1925 Cammell Laird-built motor car weighed over 33 tons. The lighter construction did cause trouble in later years as the seat risers inside the cars had to be reinforced because of the development of fractures; and in addition the body bolsters also began to fracture and had to be replaced.

This batch of vehicles was not in fact delivered until 1929/30 but in the records and by general usage they were known as the 1927 Feltham stock; on the car treadover plates the date 1928 appeared. Forty-nine of the motor cars were allocated initially to the Piccadilly, 20 of which were in fact modified to replace the converted French motor cars to run with the original Cammell Laird trailer cars, allowing the trains to be worked by two men.

The remainder of the cars enabled the gate stock trains to be withdrawn from the Piccadilly and the Bakerloo Lines. The last gate stock train ran in passenger service on the Piccadilly Line in June 1929 and on the Bakerloo Line in the early hours of 1 January 1930.

*Below:*
**The 'porter's plunger' fitted to control trailer cars to close the doors of a section of the train from the platform.** *LRT U27406*

# 9. Standard Stock Again 1929/30

In 1929, 18 motor cars, 17 trailer cars and 18 control trailers were ordered from the Union Construction Co for the Piccadilly Line. This block of stock provided eight six-car trains and enabled the Cammell Laird stock — the original air door stock — to be transferred to the Bakerloo Line. The Cammell Laird cars were in fact not sufficiently weatherproof for operation for long periods in the open sections of the line, and the authorised extensions of the Piccadilly Line west to Hounslow and South Harrow and northwards to Cockfosters were mainly open running. There were 10 six-car trains of the original air door stock and some improvement in availability was expected from the purchase of more

Standard stock cars which could couple with the existing fleet, so the equivalent number was not purchased.

An additional experimental Standard stock six-car train was however ordered from Feltham. This was known as the 1930 Feltham stock and consisted of two motor cars and four trailer cars. This train was the prototype for the stock to be ordered for the Piccadilly Line extensions which would introduce a number of new features. These cars were in fact the last tube stock cars to be built at Feltham, the Union Construction Co factory closing on 25 March 1932. This was mainly due to political pressure from supporters of the car construction industry which insisted that a clause be inserted in the

legislation concerning the formation of the London Passenger Transport Board, to the effect that the new 'monopoly' must not be concerned with manufacture except for experimental and modification work.

The motor cars were about 1ft (305mm) longer, an additional length made possible by tapering the trailing end of the car to compensate for the additional overhang on curves. An improved type of door control box was provided at the guard's gangway. The trailer cars were 2ft (610mm) longer than the earlier Standard stock cars, as both ends could now be tapered to compensate for the overhang on curves. The trailer cars were 51ft 9½in (15.79m) long overall. Two trailer cars

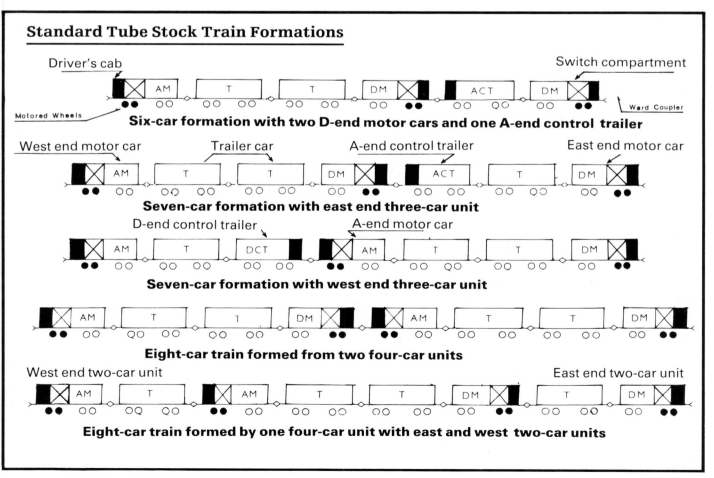

**Standard Tube Stock Train Formations**

Driver's cab | Switch compartment

Motored Wheels | Ward Coupler

**Six-car formation with two D-end motor cars and one A-end control trailer**

West end motor car | Trailer car | A-end control trailer | East end motor car

**Seven-car formation with east end three-car unit**

D-end control trailer | A-end motor car

**Seven-car formation with west end three-car unit**

**Eight-car train formed from two four-car units**

West end two-car unit | East end two-car unit

**Eight-car train formed by one four-car unit with east and west two-car units**

## 1923-29 Types Standard Tube Stock

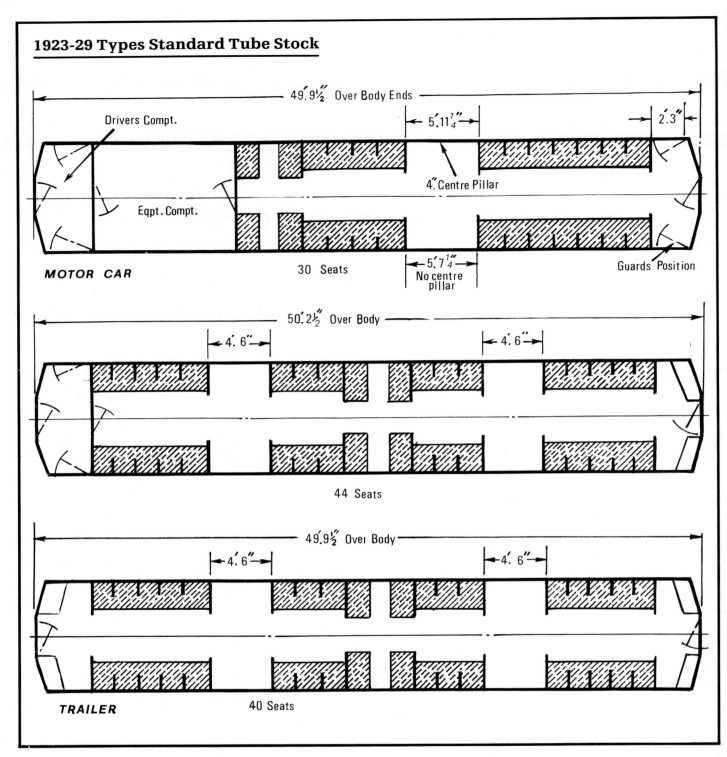

**49'.9½" Over Body Ends**

Drivers Compt.

5'.11¼"

2'.3"

4" Centre Pillar

Eqpt. Compt.

**MOTOR CAR**

30 Seats

5'.7¼"
No centre
pillar

Guards' Position

**50'.2½" Over Body**

4'. 6"

4'. 6"

44 Seats

**49'.9½" Over Body**

4'.6"

4'. 6"

**TRAILER**

40 Seats

continued to have only two pairs of double doors, openings widened from 4ft 6in to 5ft 2in. There was the same seating as in the previous Standard trailer cars. The other two trailer cars in this experimental train were of a modified design, having end doors as well as two pairs of double doors on each side. These double doors remained at 4ft 6in (1.372m) opening and the single door at half this width.

The seating capacity of the two trailer cars with additional doors to facilitate loading was reduced from 48 to 40, but subsequently four peak-hour occasional seats of the fold-down type were added at the end gangways.

A sliding door was provided at the guard's end of these two experimental motor cars in place of the swing door, but the bulkhead between the passenger saloon and the guard's gangway was maintained. The door control panels were placed on this bulkhead so the guard now faced the rear of the train when working the position. This arrangement was not perpetuated in subsequent stocks as it was considered that the guard working the position should always face towards the front of the train; but with the door control boxes in this position and not on the end bulkhead it was difficult to take up this position.

Although stock for the Piccadilly Line had not previously been fitted with heaters, this experimental train was so provided in anticipation of the extension to Cockfosters and South Harrow. Given to the introduction of this train was a good deal of publicity emphasising the British materials used in its construction, because of the serious industrial depression which was gripping the country at the time. In fact for several years this train while working as a unit was known as the 'All British' train. It was operated in service both on the Piccadilly Line and on the Morden-Edgware Line (now the Northern Line). Transfer between the lines was facil-

# 1931 Type Standard Tube Stock

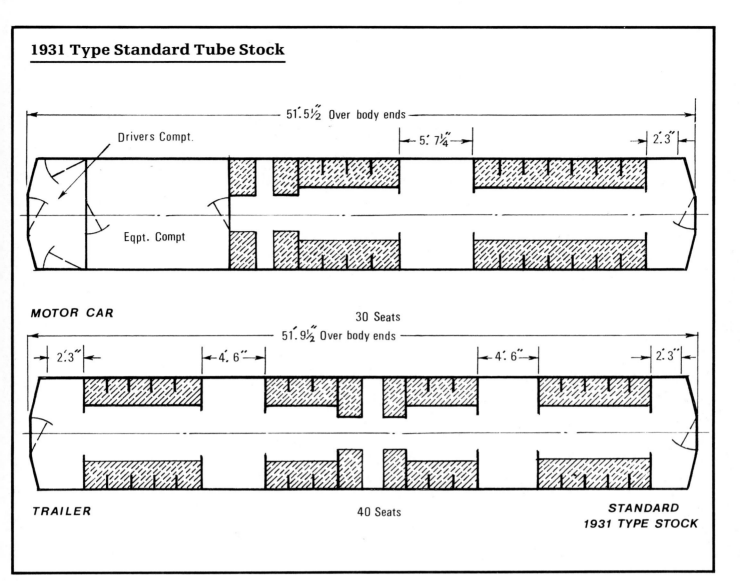

51'5½" Over body ends

Drivers Compt.

Eqpt. Compt.

5' 7¼"    2'3"

**MOTOR CAR**    30 Seats

51'9½" Over body ends

2'3"    4' 6"    4' 6"    2'3"

**TRAILER**    40 Seats    **STANDARD 1931 TYPE STOCK**

itated by the completion of the junction at King's Cross on 27 March 1927; up to this time all rolling stock transfers to Golders Green depot had to be made by road. Trials on the Morden-Edgware Line were considered desirable at this time because there was a greater concentration of traffic, which gave better testing facilities for the new door arrangement.

Following the introduction of this stock an order was placed with the newly-formed Metropolitan-Cammell Carriage Wagon & Finance Co Ltd, which was an amalgamation of two of the car building firms previously competing for Underground rolling stock orders, namely Cammell Laird and Metropolitan. The stock ordered consisted of 22 motor cars, 20 trailers and 20 control trailers to make up six-car trains to replace the Watford Joint stock on the Bakerloo, because some Standard stock trains and the Cammell Laird cars were now working the 'Local' Bakerloo service, which emphasised the relatively poor station working of the Watford Joint stock. The average comparison of timings of station stopping time was that the Watford Joint stock trains took more than 30 seconds at

every stop against 20 seconds with the new air-door trains. Such a difference could make as much as two minutes in the schedule between Elephant and Queens Park. Conversion of the stock to air doors was considered but the cars were not structurally suitable. A decision was therefore taken to replace them, and this was reinforced by a fatal accident caused by a passenger getting caught in the swing doors in a way that was not fully detected by the interlock feature.

Although the Watford Joint stock was only 10 years old, the advantage to be achieved from improved staffing arrangements and track occupation time was so great that withdrawal was justified. The replacement cars included two major technical improvements in addition to the air-door operation — electro-pneumatic brakes and weak field control. Both these features were considered to be an important feature for the longer higher speed runs to Watford. They had of course been provided in the experimental 'All British' train built at Feltham.

When the Watford Replacement stock entered service the agreement concern-

ing joint working was modified, because to become a mileage payment for the tube trains working beyond Queens Park, the new rolling stock was owned entirely by Underground group. This is still the basis of the operation.

The platform heights on the Watford Line were adjusted to the compromise height of 2ft 9in (838mm) so that the car floors on the Watford Replacement stock did not need to be placed at a special height. The motor cars were again provided with 'Y' trucks and 40in (1.016m) wheels and therefore fitted with WT54-type traction motors with a gear ratio of 16:67.

The main feature which made these cars rather special and necessitated their retention for a long time as a special fleet was the electro-pneumatic brake which required additional train wires and the provision of another 10-core control jumper, although at this time not all the 30 wires passing through the train from end to end were used.

The electro-pneumatic (EP) brake was superimposed upon the Westinghouse air brake, which was retained for all safety functions such as the deadman's

*Above:*

**Ex-London Transport Pre-1938 Tube stock was transferred to the Isle of Wight in 1967. Southern Region Isle of Wight Class 485 EMUs Nos 042 and 045 emerge from Ryde Tunnel on 9 August 1986.** *David Brown*

handle, the passenger emergency alarm and the tripcock. The EP brake required the provision of a 52V battery to supply the control. Operation of any of these safety devices applied the Westinghouse brake. For normal service stopping, however, the compressed air was applied to the brake cylinders on each car directly from the main air supply by means of electrically-operated valves energised from the EP brake controller. An additional safety feature known as the 'interlock' circuit was added, which if broken applied the Westinghouse brake. When the EP brake was operated, this circuit was interlocked with the electrical valves applying the brakes, and monitored that they had functioned correctly. A failure of the EP brake therefore automatically applied the Westinghouse brake without further guidance from the driver. This arrangement was altered many years later to give an audible warning rather than an automatic application of the brakes, so that the driver then had to apply the Westinghouse brake by further manipulation of the EP brake controller.

In addition, the Watford Replacement stock trains were the first trains to be fitted with automatic

weakening of the motor field to obtain the higher speeds which were required on the Watford Line. This weak field switching could not be cut out as it was part of the automatic notching sequence, being selected after full parallel had been achieved. The weakening of the motor fields coupled with the large wheels and the gear ratio helped these trains to equal the running performance of the Watford Joint stock in spite of the fact that they were only powered by four WT54 motors as against six GE212 type for the same length of train.

The EP brake was also considered to contribute to the improved train performance, enabling better headways to be achieved, so it was decided that all Standard stock would be converted. This conversion work was not completed until 1936.

In 1932 extra trains were required on the Watford service and some adjustment in the Standard stock holdings on the different lines was arranged by

transfers, but those allocated to the Bakerloo Line were fitted with EP brakes and weak field switching before running on the line. A total of 26 six-car trains operating the Watford service — which included some trains working to Harrow & Wealdstone only — were required. From June 1932 until November 1937 the Watford line trains were provided with a blue band 6in (152mm) deep along the middle of the cars at the waist rail, which at the time earned them the nickname 'Blue Band Margarine' trains. During the time of the conversion of the Standard stock to EP brakes it was necessary to segregate the stocks, and white diamonds were painted on the coupling ends to guide the shunters making up train sets. The Cammell Laird stock running on the Bakerloo was never converted to EP brakes so that the Standard stock motor cars running with them were not fitted with the EP brake until 1938 when the Cammell Laird cars were withdrawn from passenger service.

# 10. The Last of the Standard Stock

With Government aid, plans were made in 1929 for the extension of the Piccadilly Line northward from Finsbury Park to Cockfosters (a distance of 7½ miles) and for the projection at the other end of the line beyond Hammersmith to Acton Town on tracks independent of the District Line. The formerly disused viaduct of the Southern Railway which parallels the District tracks to Turnham Green was taken over by the Underground and extended to Acton Town to provide a four-track system between Hammersmith and Acton Town, allowing the Piccadilly Line trains to run non-stop over this section. The subsequent increase in route-miles was from 8½ to nearly 40.

In addition to these extensions, arrangements were made for the operation of seven-car instead of six-car trains. The formation of the Piccadilly Line rolling stock would therefore be similar to that already working on the Morden-Edgware Line, although some of the Standard stock had already been allocated to the Piccadilly Line, mainly to replace the gate stock. A large fleet of additional stock was now required to increase trains to seven cars and for the trains for the extensions.

The improvements provided in the 1930 experimental train were incorporated in the specification issued. More door space was provided. Not only were the guards' doors made sliding and air-operated and arranged to be used by the passengers when not required by the guard, but single sliding doors were provided at the ends of the trailer cars. The cars were built slightly longer, the overall body length of the motor car becoming 51ft 5in (15.67m). The equipment provided included the provision of the EP brake, weak field (sometimes called shunt field) control and all the safety features necessary to enable motor cars to be operated in the middle of seven-car formations. The train formation adopted as standard for the Piccadilly Line became M-T-T-M-CT-

*Below:*
**A four-car Piccadilly Line train of Standard stock on the Lillie Bridge shunting neck, including two 1931 motor cars with an air door at the guard's position, and a 1931 trailer car with end single doors as well as two pairs of double doors. An earlier trailer with no end single doors is also included in the formation.** *LRT U12068*

T-M. The three-car section was always arranged at the east end, unlike the Morden-Edgware Line where seven-car formations had the three-car section either end of the four-car portion.

An order was placed for 275 cars. All 145 motor cars were built by the Metropolitan-Cammell Carriage Wagon & Finance Co, 106 'B' end cars or east-facing cars and 39 'A' end or west-facing cars. A total of 90 trailer cars were built by the Birmingham Railway Carriage & Wagon Co Ltd and a further 40 trailers by the Gloucester Railway Carriage & Wagon Co. All the trailer cars had 12 doors: two double doors on each side with single doors at the end vestibules. No control trailers were ordered although these were required to make up the train formation. To make sufficient 'A' end control trailer cars available, some transfers were made between the Hampstead, Bakerloo and Piccadilly Lines.

In order to equate the numbers of control trailers of the right type, some 'B' end cars were turned to become 'A' end cars. In spite of the transfer of control trailers to the Piccadilly Line there was now a surplus of control trailers arising from the formation of trains into seven cars with middle motors. At this time, the Hampstead had in fact a surplus of control trailers owing to the increase of the train formations on the line from six-car to

seven-car length. These cars required to work on the Piccadilly Line were converted at Acton Works to work with the new stock: this conversion included the provision of EP brakes and car heaters. The existing Piccadilly Line Standard stock was converted to run with the new cars and included the fitting of weak field control. (The weak field was also called shunt field control because the weak field was obtained by shunting the main field coils of the motors, thereby reducing the magnetic field and thus increasing the top speed.)

Weak field control was considered very successful in improving scheduled speeds; and this arrangement was applied to the Morden-Edgware Line, which enabled a saving of four trains at peak periods without loss of service frequency. Significant savings in the total rolling stock needed were also achieved by applying this principle from the outset to the extended Piccadilly Line.

After the formation of the London Passenger Transport Board in 1933, arrangements were made for the Piccadilly Line service to be extended from South Harrow to Uxbridge over the tracks of the Metropolitan Railway, which had now become part of the total Underground management. Eight additional seven-car trains were now required to meet the additional train service which resulted. In order to provide these, an order was placed with Metropolitan-Cammell for only 26 new motor cars: 10 'A' end and 16 'B' end cars. Some further transfers of cars between lines were then arranged to enable the number of trains for the increased Piccadilly Line service to be provided. These 1934 stock cars were the last of the Standard stock cars to be built and were distinguishable from the 1931 stock only by an expert.

Ten of the 1934 stock motor cars were fitted with roller bearing axle boxes, the first tube cars to be so fitted when purchased. Oiling and packing of white metal sleeve bearings of axle boxes, traction motors and traction motor suspension bearings was an onerous maintenance requirement and hardly a day passed without a bearing of some kind running hot in service. Traction motors were the first to be fitted successfully with ball and roller bearings and the motors built new for the 1931 standard stock had such bearings. All previous WT54, WT54A and MV152 motors were modified to take ball and roller bearings at Acton Works, the work being completed by the end of 1932.

Another improvement introduced at this time with the 1931 stock was the increase in the wattage of the lighting, as these cars were fitted from the beginning with 60W lamps — five in series in 600V circuits — compared with the 40W lamps used previously. This improvement was applied to all Standard stock cars, the only modifi-

*Left:*
**A six-car train of Piccadilly Line stock with a 1927 motor car built by Union Construction Co at Feltham, seen outside the depot at Lillie Bridge before the extension beyond Hammersmith. The Cromwell Road extension scheme now occupies the space between the end of the train and the Whiteley depository in the background.**

**The Feltham cars had a characteristic curve to the lower body panels. These cars were renumbered between 3028 and 3311 in the 1930 renumbering scheme and many of them ran on the Bakerloo Line until replaced by 1938 Tube stock. On the right can be seen some of the 1920 Cammell Laird trailer cars.** *LRT U7025*

*Below left:*
**Outside Golders Green depot is pictured one of a batch of 64 motor cars built by Metropolitan Carriage & Wagon Co with GEC traction equipment. This batch of cars ran on the Northern Line until replaced by 1938 Tube stock, this particular car being renumbered 3671 in the 1930 renumbering scheme.**

**The early no smoking labels in the shape of a star should be noted; this was before the roundel type was accepted as standard.** *LRT U5010*

*Above:*
**A Piccadilly Line Standard stock motor car with the wartime splinter-proof netting on the windows (including the specially prepared look-out section) and the 'reading' lights in the ceiling.** *LRT U34183*

*Below:*
**The outside view of the switch compartment of a Pre-1938 Tube stock showing the contactor bank which was replaced by the PCM traction control unit in the 1938 Tube stock.** *LRT 24095*

cation required to achieve this, being an increase in the fuse rating of the circuits.

As the 1931/34 cars were designed from the start for EP brakes for which a low-voltage supply was required, space was found in the equipment chamber for the 52V battery. Cars subsequently converted to EP braking had this battery placed under a seat in the passenger saloon. Each motor car was provided with a charging resistance which connected the 600V supply to the battery when the driver's control position was not in use. Special care had to be taken to see that batteries did not operate for too long in middle motor or control trailer car positions, to prevent damage from overcharging of the batteries.

With the advent of the 1931 stock a renumbering scheme for all Underground stock in one series was introduced. The Piccadilly Line cars were renumbered in this scheme first, 'A' motor cars starting from 3000 with even numbers and 'B' motor cars from 3001 with odd numbers. Similarly, control trailers were numbered from 5000 and trailer cars (which of course were not handed) from 7000. The Bakerloo Line cars and then the Morden-Edgware Line cars followed, with the odd cars such as the Central London cars at the end of the series, where the motor cars began at 3912, the control trailers 5928 and the trailers 7911. This numbering scheme was only carried out as the cars were repaired or when they passed through Acton Works, taking 2½ years to complete. In fact the last car was not renumbered until the end of 1935.

As early as 1907, brake blocks made of impregnated cotton had been used on tube rolling stock but had been confined to tunnel working because the material was not suitable for sustained braking under wet conditions. By 1930, however, an asbestos fibre moulded under pressure had been developed, which overcame to a large extent the problem of reduced brake power under wet conditions. Under the trade name Ferodo it was again tested on tube train services. In 1931 a seven-car Morden-Edgware train was equipped with this type of material for the brake blocks on all trailing wheels, while the motor wheels retained the cast iron brake shoes. This train was identified by a yellow painted square containing the letters FE on each external corner of the driving cabs and these cars were kept together for prolonged testing, being the last to be renumbered, in 1935. The result of this test was that Standard stock again received a general modification to the brake rigging on motor cars to enable Ferodo blocks (or composition blocks as they were subsequently called) to be fitted to the trailing truck, balancing the braking forces from the single brake cylinder between the motor and trailing bogies. While this modification was being undertaken, cars again had to be segregated because the brake pressures used were different, and service coupling was incompatible.

*Below:*
**A Pre-1938 Tube stock (Standard stock) motor car being loaded on to Isle of Wight ferry on its way to the Isle of Wight Railway. This was the 'D' car for the set and was originally a 1931 stock car from the Piccadilly Line, numbered 3185.** *Alan Barter*

# 11. Pre-1938 Tube Stock

The extensions and alterations of the Central Line in the 1935/40 New Works Programme were much more extensive than those of the Northern and Bakerloo Lines. The work included platform lengthening to enable eight-car trains to be operated and alterations to the original tunnels to accommodate the LT fourth-rail system. Even if the war had not intervened to delay the new works, the Central Line extensions would have taken much longer than on the other two lines.

The rolling stock programme was arranged so that when the 1938 Tube stock began operating on the Northern and Bakerloo, the Standard stock released was to be passed through Acton Works for conversion and modernisation for use on the Central Line, allowing the old Central London rolling stock to be scrapped.

The war interrupted this programme so that many cars were actually stored for the duration, mainly at Hainault and Ruislip depots, new depots constructed to serve the extended Central Line. Sufficient cars were converted initially to enable the old Central Line stock to be withdrawn and replaced with Standard stock which now became re-designated Pre-1938 Tube stock. At first these cars were made into six-car formations and modified for current collection from a centre positive rail with an earth return until all the original cars were withdrawn. The last Central London Railway type car ran on 10 June 1939 and the changeover to fourth-rail traction system came on 4 May 1940, a postponement from the original date of 20 April.

The modernisation of the Standard stock consisted of a number of equipment changes including the fitting of retardation control to the EP brake, which enabled higher braking rates to be provided which in turn enabled closer headways to be arranged. A weak field flag switch was also fitted which enabled a higher speed to be selected on the outer sections of the Central Line, when the extensions were completed, but kept the top speed down in the congested tunnel sections.

The cars were also fitted with passenger door control which involved the provision of an additional door circuit operated at 50V superimposed on the original 600V door circuits. The passenger-open circuit needed an additional operating key and a special battery and was set up by the guard pressing an additional button on his panel. This button was provided with a flap to prevent inadvertent operation. When this button had been operated the doors could be opened by a passenger pressing the push buttons provided at each doorway, the opening being limited to that doorway. The passenger-operated push buttons were fitted both outside and inside.

The maintenance of this door equipment was heavy, and although re-introduced after the end of World War 2, passenger door control was withdrawn from use following a fire which occurred at Holland Park on the Central Line in July 1958. The removal of the additional operating key at any time prevented adequate communication between the driver and guard and this was considered to be a contributory cause of the incident and an unacceptable hazard in emergency circumstances. Although this criticism could not be applied to the 1938 Tube stock circuits, the passenger door opening feature was withdrawn from all stock after March 1959.

The first Pre-1938 Tube stock train modified to the new standards and complete with passenger door control entered service on the Northern Line in April 1938. The first run through the Central Line with Pre-1938 Tube stock took place on 12 November 1938. When Pre-1938 Tube stock operated on the Central Line at first it covered only the same sections and the same duties as the old stock. The trains were originally made up into six-car trains with three motor cars, but until the power supply was improved the accelerating relays were set at a low value, and one motor car was cut out on the trains which operated between Wood Lane and Ealing Broadway. This arrangement remained operative until the extension

and improvement work was introduced after the end of hostilities. The new White City station was brought into use on 23 November 1947 following which the Central Line trains were increased to seven-car length.

The Central Line services on the extensions were built up gradually after the end of the war. The first passenger train ran over the new tube extension beyond Liverpool Street to Stratford on 4 December 1946, with six-car train formations running until the new White City station replaced the old Wood Lane station which had restricted the working to six cars. A year later, on 14 December 1947, the service was extended to Newbury Park and Woodford; and at this time, too, 12 peak-hour trains were increased to eight-car length. The eight-car formation was at this time made up by coupling two four-car portions together. Tube trains began running to West Ruislip — completing the Western extension — and to Loughton and Hainault on 21 November 1948. The final extension of the main line to Epping was made on 25 September 1949. As the traffic increased, the seven-car formations were inadequate, especially at the peak hours, so more eight-car formations were provided as Pre-1938 Tube stock could be released. This came first from the Bakerloo and then the Piccadilly as further new stock became available, first of all by the introduction of the 1949 Tube stock and finally by the 1959 Tube stock.

The normal formation of an eight-car train at this time was M-T-T-M × M-T-T-M, and control trailers were not required in this formation. Thus a number of control trailers became surplus to operating requirements and were used as trailers. The control equipment was in fact removed and these cars became known as 'demob-bed' control trailers. Later, a number of these cars were converted completely to trailers by the removal of the cab door and the provision of four additional seats in the abandoned cab. The bulkhead was not removed but openings were cut to avoid the total

enclosure of the area. These seats however were somewhat exclusive and were referred to as 'lovers' seats'.

The eight-car train formation formed of two four-car portions was delayed at busy stations because of the blank space in the middle of the platform caused by the two motor cabs coming together, making a length of almost 50ft without a passenger doorway. Arrangements were therefore made in 1961 for the eight-car train formation to be altered to operate M-T × M-T-T-M × T-M. By February 1959 some 52 trains were operating as eight-car trains and the remaining seven-car trains became the operating problem because they were inadequate to deal with the traffic at busy stations expecting an eight-car formation. Any service disorganisation was then accentuated by seven-car train working. The advent of the 1959 Tube stock enabled the Piccadilly Line Pre-1938 Tube stock to be transferred to the Central Line, so by 25 July 1960 a total of 81 eight-car trains were being operated in service. The first 1931/34 cars ran on the Central Line in January 1960, providing trailer cars with 12 doors, and air doors at the guard's position of motor cars. The operation of this type of train accentuated the inferiority of the older Pre-1938 Tube stock.

By this time there was significant passenger reaction to the continued problem of the operation of Pre-1938 Tube stock, and after the first 19 trains of 1959 Tube stock had entered service on the Piccadilly Line it was decided to begin putting new stock on the Central Line. The decision had been accelerated by another serious incident with Pre-1938 Tube stock involving electrical fire damage. An incident at Redbridge in August 1960 caused the removal of all power receptacle boxes used for depot movements from middle motors cars and in consequence drico equipment and EP brake batteries rendering the cars completely inflexible. This arrangement was applied to the cars operating on the Piccadilly Line as well as the Central Line. In view of this a decision was taken to replace the whole of the Pre-1938 Tube stock fleet, and some of the 1931/34 vintage trains from the Piccadilly Line were transferred as complete eight-car formations without the conversion of the 12V emergency lighting circuit — including, of course, the 'loudaphone' driver to guard communication arrangement — to 50V to make them compatible with existing Central Line stock. The prohibition concerning coupling only affected motor cars, as trailer cars could be formed into either type of train providing the emergency lighting bulbs were changed from 50V to 12V or vice versa.

The last Pre-1938 Tube stock train ran on the Central Line on 22 June 1963 and on the Piccadilly Line in June 1964. On the Northern City Line between Moorgate and Finsbury Park however, the stock remained on public services until 8 November 1966 when it was replaced by 1938 Tube stock. The Great Northern & City Railway became an isolated part of the Northern Line on Monday 15 May 1939 and was subsequently designated Northern City Line after the previous weekend's conversion of the line to the London Transport four-rail system and the signalling arrangements. The old rolling stock had had a train-stop fail-safe arrangement but it was carried on the car roof and was of antiquated design. Over the weekend the old stock had been removed and Pre-1938 Tube stock brought in by way of Highgate Wood sidings from Golders Green depot. The stock consisted of eight six-car sets of the formation M-T-T-CT × CT-M, with the two-car portion at the south end of the train but operating on its own in the off-peak.

Arising out of the Victoria Line reconstruction work at Finsbury Park, the Northern & City service was curtailed at Drayton Park, and on 4 October 1964 the 1923/27 cars of Pre-1938 Tube stock were replaced by 1931/34 type cars released from the Piccadilly Line by the introduction of 1959 Tube stock. They were now not wanted on the Central Line because of the decision to replace all the Pre-1938 Tube stock as soon as possible. A few of the motor cars had to be renumbered to avoid confusion with the numbering scheme adopted for the new Victoria Line stock — the 1967 Tube stock.

The operation of two-car trains in the off-peak involved coupling and uncoupling at Finsbury Park, so that when this facility was removed by the cut-back to Drayton Park the 1931/34 cars were made up into eight four-car units which maintained the service over the whole of the traffic day. An additional 16 trailers were stored in part of the disused tunnels between Drayton Park and Finsbury Park. These trailers were earmarked to increase the operating units to five or six-car sets if traffic so demanded. In the event they were not required and these cars were scrapped without further passenger service when the Pre-1938 Tube stock was replaced on the line in 1966 by 1938 Tube stock.

The first allocation on the Bakerloo of 1938 Tube stock almost required an equal number of Pre-1938 Tube stock trains to operate as well. Twenty-four seven-car trains were to be provided by Pre-1938 Tube stock and 23 seven-car trains by new 1938 Tube stock containing some of the '58' trailers. Later it was decided that all the '58' trailers should be allocated to the Bakerloo and the Pre-1938 Tube stock allocation was reduced to 19 seven-car trains. These trains were all required to have the three-car position at the West End with two 'A' end motor cars in the train formation. In order to get the right proportion of motor cars some had to be turned and renumbered when passing through Acton Works. The work required to turn Pre-1938 Tube stock motor cars involved some rewiring as the jumper receptacle boxes had to be repositioned and the main and train line hosepipes had to be switched. After seven-car trains began operating on the Stanmore Line, some overcrowding problems arose with Pre-1938 Tube stock, and the formation was altered to M-M-T-CT × CT-T-M to place both 'A' motor cars at the leading end of the trains. All the Pre-1938 Tube stock was withdrawn from the Bakerloo on 23 May 1949.

After the withdrawal of the Pre-1938 Tube stock trains, the '58' trailers remained operational with the 1938 Tube stock fleet, together with trailer cars converted to operate with the 1935 stock units and the later 1960 Tube stock. The breed is still operational — albeit in modified form — between Ryde and Shanklin on the Isle of Wight, as some of the withdrawn vehicles were sold to British Rail to make up trains to operate on this special service in March 1967.

In addition, car No 3327, which entered service in 1929, is preserved in South Kensington Science Museum. Other motor cars were converted to run as ballast motors to power works trains, joining the miscellaneous vehicle fleet.

# 12.   The Experimental Streamlined Stock 1935

The formation of the London Passenger Transport Board in 1933 made it possible to embark on large-scale planning for Underground extensions. The 1935/40 New Works Programme envisaged, among other things, the extension of the Morden-Edgware Line northwards from Highgate to enable through running on the London & North Eastern Railway tracks to Edgware and High Barnet and for the incorporation of the Great Northern & City Railway into this system by projection over the London & North Eastern tracks from Finsbury Park to join the main line at East Finchley. World War 2 intervened before all these proposals were completed and part of the project was later abandoned, but the Morden-Edgware Line was renamed the Northern Line in 1937 in anticipation of completion of these new works. Tube trains began running to High Barnet on 14 April 1940.

In addition, the 1935/40 New Works Programme included extensions to the Central London Railway, which was renamed the Central Line at the same time. The Central Line extensions were alongside the Great Western Railway tracks to West Ruislip in the west and from Liverpool Street eastwards in new tube tunnels to link up with London & North Eastern Railway tracks at Leytonstone and Newbury Park and so reach Hainault, Woodford, Loughton

and Epping. The work on the Central Line included a realigning of the original Central London railway tunnels to enable trains of normal tube stock dimensions to be operated, as well as lengthening the platforms to take eight cars instead of six. The Central Line extensions, which involved considerable engineering work, were curtailed because of the war. Most of the proposals were subsequently completed, but the last section of the main line from Loughton to Epping was not operated by tube stock until 25 September 1949.

To serve these considerable extensions of mileage, a considerable quantity of additional rolling stock was needed. In 1935, four six-car trains of an experimental nature were ordered from the Metropolitan-Cammell Carriage & Wagon Co. These trains incorporated many new features but the two principal requirements were increased passenger accommodation and improved traction performance. All the electrical equipment was located beneath the underframe, avoiding the necessity of providing the switch compartment over the motor bogies, and

thus providing increased passenger space. Accommodation in a six-car train then provided the equivalent of a seven-car train of Standard stock. Because a motor car was not now wasteful of passenger space, more motor cars could be provided in a train and therefore improve the performance. The experimental trains were provided in a six-car formation composed of two-car units, all motor cars.

Before the final design of the 1935 tube was settled, a number of equipment and operating experiments had been conducted. A 1923 control trailer was fitted experimentally with a streamlined end. Two other cars were fitted with Tomlinson couplers which provided automatic coupling mechanically, electrically and pneumatically, these being a modified version of a coupling already in use on American tramway systems for the multiple operation of street cars. Another trailer car was fitted with air conditioning equipment. Modified versions of these experiments — with many others — were included on the 1935 stock.

With the advent of this stock the 'B' end cars were redesignated 'D' end cars

---

*Below:*
**Non-streamlined two-car 1935 stock as built, seen outside Northfields depot. The Metro-Vick units were provided with flat fronts and were the precursors of the 1938 Tube stock. As air conditioning was not provided, drop lights were fitted.** *LRT U25310*

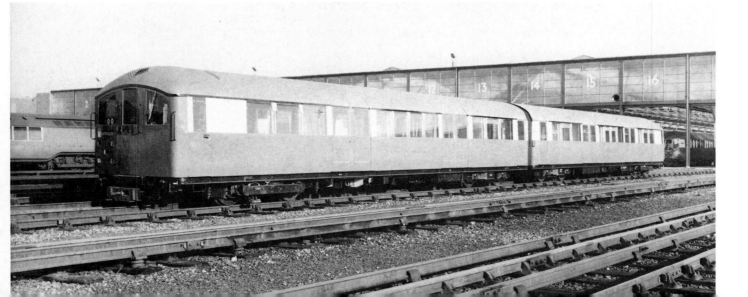

to conform with the nomenclature adopted for the four axles of a car. The car axles were lettered A, B, C and D from the west end ('A' end) of a car; the other end naturally became the 'D' end and motor cars facing this way became 'D' cars instead of 'B' cars. This nomenclature was applied henceforward to all existing rolling stock.

By motorising 50% of the axles, arranging for a greater proportion of the train weight to be available for adhesion, and by introducing a multi-notch system of traction control which by cutting out the starting resistance in smaller steps reduced the peak currents so that the accelerating current could approach nearer the wheel-slipping point, the train acceleration was raised from 1.2mph/sec of the Standard stock seven-car train to 2mph/sec on the six-car experimental trains.

The braking rate was also increased to the equivalent of 3mph/sec by an entirely new arrangement of wheel braking. Each brake shoe was provided with an individual brake cylinder mounted on the truck frame. Each cylinder was provided with its own slack adjuster so that the shoe wear was automatically taken up. The normal braking control provided was electro-pneumatic, incorporating for the first time a self-lapping driver's brake controller, together with retardation control. The retardation controller enabled the deceleration of the train to be maintained at constant level throughout the speed range, thus allowing higher brake cylinder pressure to be applied initially when the coefficient of friction was low between the brake shoe and the wheel, and for this pressure to be eased off as this coefficient increased, so preventing

*Above:*
**A streamlined two-car unit of 1935 stock as built. This unit, the first of the group, was originally provided with a form of air conditioning, and no drop lights were provided, giving a smooth external finish.** *LRT U22057A*

*Bottom:*
**The original streamlined unit car Nos 10000-11000 on test between South Ealing and Acton Town.** *LRT 19595*

wheel pick-up. The retardation controller consisted of a set of two glass tubes containing mercury placed in the line of track. The movement of the mercury in the tubes was arranged to 'make' and 'break' the electric circuits which controlled the appropriate pneumatic brake operating valves to avoid excessive brake application.

All the Type C200 traction motors were manufactured by Crompton Parkinson, being specially designed to go into the limited space under the car floor, which was sloped over the bogies to provide additional space. The motors were rated at 138hp, and only one was

fitted to each bogie, mounted on the inner axle. For the first time on tube rolling stock the motor was mounted on a roller suspension sleeve fitted on the motor axle. The bogies were of all-welded construction, with a wheelbase of 6ft 3in (1.905m), but the outer axle was 3ft 6in (1.067m) from the centreline compared with the inner axle's 2ft 9in (838mm), thus ensuring that the greatest load was on the motored axle. This asymmetric bogie enabled 58% of the car weight to be available for adhesion.

The C200 motor was specially designed with a long armature and flat case so that the floor of the car had to be raised only a small amount; this was produced by a small slope and therefore the car floor was stepless.

Each of the four six-car trains was provided with a traction control system devised by a different concern, but it was specified that no matter how different they were in detail, they were required to work in multiple.

In collaboration with Allen West & Co Ltd, Crompton Parkinson produced three different schemes. The two-car unit given the numbers 10000-11000 had a series-parallel system using two face plate controllers, one in each motor circuit, driven by a 50V motor. This system produced 57 accelerating notches.

The two-car unit given the numbers 10001-11001 had each pair of motors in permanent parallel and here again the resistance was cut out by a face plate controller, also driven by a 50V motor.

The third Crompton two-car unit was actually numbered 10005-11005, having a motor-driven camshaft replacing the two face plate controllers to provide the series parallel connection of two motors.

All the units provided by the General Electric Co (numbered 10002-11002, 10004-11004 and 10006-11006) had similar equipments utilising a motor-driven camshaft to provide the series parallel connection of each pair of traction motors. The camshaft had to make three revolutions from off to full weak field with electro-pneumatic contactors making the power switching as required. One of the units was arranged to have the motors in permanent parallel, which simplified the switching. A technical feature of the GEC system was that the movement of the camshaft was controlled by a time base with only an overriding overload current control.

To meet the special requirements of tube train operation, the British Thomson Houston-equipped units numbered 10003-11003, 10007-11007 and 10008-11008 were provided with equipment only slightly modified from that already operating in New York. This equipment was the famous PCM which was also a camshaft-operated design, but the driving force was oil under pressure rather than an electric motor. One of the most important advantages of the PCM arrangement, which made it more reliable in operation than any of the others, was the fact that 'full parallel' position coincided with the 'off' position of the camshaft, and once the full sequence had been achieved the camshaft did not have to run back.

The Metropolitan-Vickers scheme, applied to units 10009-11009, 10010-11010 and 10011-11011, used an oil-driven power drum for performing all the resistance switching, giving a total of 45 notches. The drum was driven slowly round but had to be stopped accurately under the control of the current. The main switching was achieved by electro-pneumatic contactors but in spite of this the main drum contacts were not protected against severe fusing.

All these traction control equipments required a low-voltage supply for control purposes, and a 5kW motor generator set providing 50V was installed on one car of each two-car unit. This supply was also used for the car lighting, enabling the lamps to be low-wattage 50V types, all in parallel. No emergency lights were required because a 50V battery was arranged to float across the generator, remaining available when the motor generator shut down.

The length of the cars was 52ft 5in (15.98m) with seats for 40 passengers and additional tip-up seats at the ends away from the driving cab. The outer end of all the two-car units of three of the trains were semi-streamlined, providing a semi-elliptical cab which enabled the driver to be placed in the centre in an armchair seat with the brake and master controller handles arranged like aeroplane joysticks. This arrangement did not prove popular with operating crews but as it was proved that speeds approaching 80mph were required before streamlining produced any material effect on power consumption, the fourth train, that with Metropolitan-Vickers equipment, was designed with a conventional cab and vertical controller.

The cars of each unit were semi-permanently coupled together and could not normally be parted except in the depot workshops, so that the two

*Below:*
**The interior of 1935 stock, looking towards the trailing end. The arrangement of the double seating in the centre section was continued in the 1938 Tube stock layout.**
*LRT U21909*

*Bottom:*
**The view inside a streamlined car cab with the driver's armchair seat reversed.**
*LRT U21912*

cars always worked together, unlike the Standard stock where the cars were individually coupled. The two-car units were coupled together to form a train by means of a new type of automatic coupler known as the Wedglock — developed from the experimental Tomlinson coupler — which coupled the units together mechanically, electrically and pneumatically.

The first unit, 10000-11000, was provided with double-glazing, the normal drop-type ventilators being eliminated. The cars were fitted with an experimental system of forced ventilation to provide a continual supply of fresh filtered air, thermostatically controlled and heated, if necessary, from the 600V traction supply. This system had however to be abandoned as any failure of the controls very quickly caused discomfort to passengers, especially in the tube tunnels.

The compressors provided were of two different types based on designs from tramcars. One type manufactured by the Electro Mechanical Brake Co, Type 36H4, a four-cylinder reciprocating compressor, was fitted to five units. The other units were fitted with a rotary compressor based on Swiss Locomotive Manufacturing Co design Type KLL4.

The driving position on the streamlined units caused some very interesting features to be incorporated in the cars. Although the car ends were streamlined, provision had to be made for passengers to be detrained through the front and for passage between units when they were coupled together. Several different methods of opening this door were incorporated in the different units, including sliding back on rails. In order to perform shunting and coupling duties adequately, shunting buttons which could be reached in the standing position were provided. Operation of these buttons allowed inching either forward or reverse to make coupling easy.

A feature of the guard's controls was the provision of only one 'open' button on each side; protection against inadvertent operation was provided by a hinged flap over the button.

The experimental units went into service on the Piccadilly in six-car formation to gain operating experience. The streamlined units were not segregated, being mixed in the six-car formations, while the non-streamlined Metro-Vick unit was retained as a train. However, the trains experienced many teething troubles and when World War 2 broke out maintenance became difficult, so all the experimental cars were stored for the duration. Three of the cars were used as ARP (Air Raid Precaution) shelters, being sandbagged over a pit road for emergency use, one at Northfields and the other two at Cockfosters. The 24 cars remained stored until the end of 1948 when it was decided to convert the streamlined ones

to trailer cars for operation with the 1938 Tube stock, for which they had been the experimental prototypes.

In 1949 the non-streamlined units were rehabilitated and converted to operate as two-car shuttle units for the Central Line. The automatic couplers at the driving ends of the cars were replaced with Ward mechanical couplers only, so that it would be possible to couple to the Standard stock then running on the Central Line. Air-connecting hoses and passenger open door push buttons were also fitted. In

addition, the MV control equipment was removed and replaced by the BTH equipment, released from the cars being converted to trailers. The guard's control was removed from the cabs and replaced at the trailing end of the 'D' cars only. The guard's control remained at one position on the two-car units irrespective of the direction of travel. Compressors of the KLL4-type were fitted on all six motor cars so that two compressors were provided on a service operating unit. These cars were used initially on the Ongar shuttle service.

*Below:*
**The view underneath a 1935 car fitted with the faceplate type of controller.**
*LRT U21914*

*Bottom:*
**A 1935 Tube stock bogie (which formed the basis for the bogies for 1938 Tube stock) featuring all-welded main frames including a 'bay window' for the extended bolster to improve the riding quality. The single traction motor and the 'maximum traction' truck formation can be seen.** *LRT U21910*

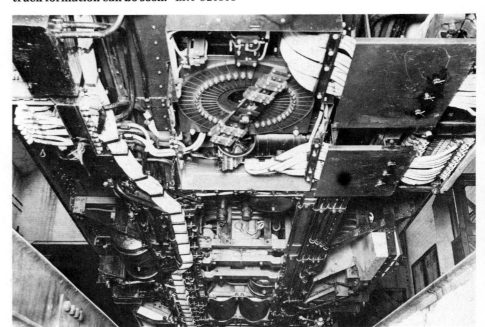

# 13.  1938 Tube Stock

The 1935/40 New Works Programme of improvements to transport in London undertaken by the recently formed London Passenger Transport Board in collaboration with the main line railways — particularly the London & North Eastern Railway and the Great Western Railway — necessitated the provision of a large number of new cars, mostly for tube line service. Following the construction of the four experimental trains, an order was placed with the Metropolitan-Cammell Carriage & Wagon Co for 751 cars and with the Birmingham Railway Carriage & Wagon Co for 370 cars. All the cars supplied by Metro-Cammell were motor cars: 644 of these were driving motor cars with motorman's cabs and 107 were non-driving motor cars — cars with traction motors and control equipment but no driving positions.

The non-driving motor car was a type of vehicle introduced to tube rolling stock fleets for the first time and enabled the number of power cars in a train to be increased without providing a driving cab, wasteful of passenger accommodation when not in use. All the new trailer cars required to make up the trains were provided by the Birmingham company, which also provided a further 99 non-driving motor cars.

In addition, to complete the fleet of new trains to be made up into six- and seven-car trains, a further 58 trailer cars were required. This number of 1927 Birmingham-built Standard trailer cars were converted at Acton Works to be compatible with the new stock. These cars subsequently became known as the '58' trailers.

The driving motor cars were divided into west ('A') end cars and east ('D') end cars. The 'A' cars were numbered from 10012 and the 'D' cars from 11012. As the non-driving motor cars and the trailer cars were identical in construction — the trailer cars had been designed so that they could be converted to non-driving motor cars if necessary — they were all numbered in the same series, beginning at 12000, but a trailer car was given the prefix '0', becoming 012xxx.

The converted trailers of Standard stock were not materially altered as far as the passenger was concerned (except for the improvement in the lighting) and were originally numbered 7513 to 7570, being renumbered 70513 to 70570 respectively upon conversion.

It was arranged that this new stock would take over the entire operation of the Northern Line and the remainder would provide the majority of the service on the Bakerloo Line. As part of the New Works Programme the old

original Bakerloo tunnel stations were reconstructed to take seven-car trains. The standard formation of the 1938 Tube stock therefore became seven cars divided into two semi-permanently coupled units, one of three cars and the other of four cars, with both units having a driving cab at each end. The four-car unit had a non-driving motor car as well as the two driving motor cars and a trailer.

The title Northern Line was introduced on 28 August 1937. The previous

*Below:*
**A front view of a 'D' car of 1938 Tube stock showing the 'weak field' flag switch in the switched-in position which produced the higher speed characteristic.** *LRT U27429*

title of Edgware, Highgate & Morden Line had applied at the time of the formation of London Transport and been abbreviated to Morden-Edgware Line in April 1934. There had been some difficulty in getting a comprehensive title for the line, which had previously been known as the Hampstead & City.

The new stock arrived at Golders Green depot on the Northern Line by a devious route involving delivery to London Transport property from the car builders at Warwick Avenue goods yard then by way of Lillie Bridge depot to Ealing Common depot. From there it was made up to be transferred by tube stock pilot motors through the King's Cross loop tunnel to Golders Green.

The cars were made ready for service and assembled into four- and three-car units, arrangements subsequently being made for odd-numbered driving motor cars to make up three-car units and even-numbered motor cars four-car units. All the cars that were delivered before the outbreak of World War 2 entered service on the Northern Line and those required for the Bakerloo Line were transferred subsequently.

The original disposition of the stock ordered at this time was that 110 seven-car trains would completely equip the Northern Line while 23 seven-car trains (including most of those containing the '58' trailers) would be transferred to the Bakerloo Line. A small number of six-car trains were to be formed for running on the Northern & City Line to Moorgate which was to be connected to the Barnet extension of the line, but this arrangement never materialised.

Out of the original 1,121 cars, 289 were owned by the London & North Eastern Railway which operated the High Barnet and Alexandra Park extension then being electrified and joined to the Northern Line. These lines were still to remain in the ownership of the main line railway and did so until Nationalisation on 1 January 1948, when London Transport took over these lines. These cars had an ownership plate fitted to the solebar but they were not segregated in complete trains, being mixed within the 1938 Tube stock fleet.

All the bogies and underframes of the cars were similar so that the trailer cars could easily be converted to non-driving motor cars later if a further increase in train performance was required. The all-welded bogies of the cars continued the asymmetric arrangement first introduced in the 1935 experimental stock with one Type LT100 traction motor carried on the inner axle of each motor bogie. The traction motors were manufactured in equal quantities by General Electric Co Ltd and Crompton Parkinson Ltd but were of identical design. In order to reduce the noise from the gears, both the motor pinion and the gear wheel mated in a single helical with a 7½° angle. Brake cylinders were mounted on

78

*Above:*
**The driver's position in 1938 Tube stock.** *LRT U27436*

the bogie frames, one piston for each brake block. This feature (also first introduced with the 1935 Experimental stock) removed the necessity for extensive truck brake rigging and considerably reduced the number of wearing parts.

The brakes fitted to the 1938 Tube stock were of the self-lapping interlocked electro-pneumatic type with automatic retardation. This system had several features which differed from the straight EP brake previously fitted to tube rolling stock. The self-lapping driver's brake valve provided a form of control in which the brake cylinder pressure corresponded to the position of the brake handle. The pressure was maintained automatically without the driver moving the handle after the initial application. This self-lapping feature was provided by the balance of a spring against the pressure built up in a brake cylinder of the leading car.

The retardation control also followed the prototype equipment developed for the 1935 Experimental stock consisting of two circular glass tubes ⅝in

(15.87mm) diameter about one-third full of mercury placed along the line of the car; that is, parallel to the direction of travel. When the train slowed down under the influence of braking, the mercury rose in the tubes to a predetermined height under the influence of the retardation rate of the train. The mercury completed an electrical circuit so that the contacts in one of the tubes cut off further application of the brakes, while in the other the contacts caused a release of the brakes down to a limiting level through the operation of valves (known as blowdown valves) carried on each car. The mercury moved forward as the braking retardation increased, making the necessary contacts and thereby enabling the braking rate used under normal service conditions to be as high as possible within the limits of adhesion. These features were, of course, all provided in addition to the Westinghouse automatic air brake, to which all the normal safety braking features — tripcocks, passenger emergency alarms and deadman's handle — were attached.

## 1938 Tube Stock

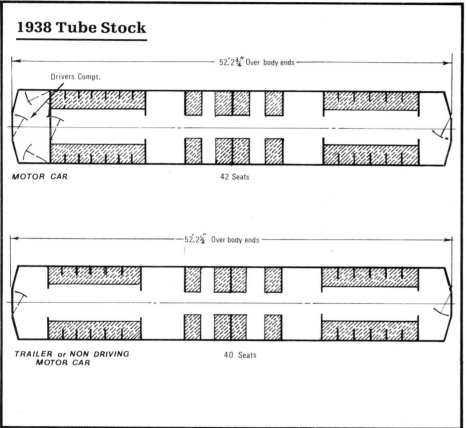

52′ 2¾″ Over body ends

Drivers Compt.

MOTOR CAR                    42 Seats

52′ 2½″ Over body ends

TRAILER or NON DRIVING
MOTOR CAR                    40 Seats

*Top:*
**A four-car Tube stock train on the Bakerloo with a converted trailer car in the make-up. Note the cream window dividers and passenger open door buttons, both features which were subsequently removed.** *LRT*

When originally ordered it was considered that the brake blocks fitted to 1938 Tube stock should be cast iron, but at the time the first trains were undergoing acceptance tests a satisfactory composition block for working under wet conditions had been produced. However, fitting these to 1938 Tube stock required a change in the braking pressure applied at the wheel and this was partly achieved by altering the brake cylinder sizes. For a time the small number of cars actually built with larger cylinders for use with cast iron blocks were kept segregated until replacement cylinders were obtained.

The PCM electrical control equipment was based on the design which had proved so effective on one set of units on the 1935 Experimental stock and was provided by BTH Co. One of the modifications incorporated was the provision of two accelerating rates, one suitable for running in the open, the other (the higher rate) for running in the tunnels where improved adhesion could be relied upon because of the dry conditions. The appropriate accelerating rate was selected by the position of the reverser drum of the master controller which had four positions — 'reverse', 'off', 'forward 1' and 'forward 2', the latter giving the higher acceleration.

To obtain higher speeds, shunt or weak field was provided, but this mode had to be selected by means of the operation of a flag switch visible from outside the driver's cab to ensure that this arrangement was selected only over the sections of the track suitable for the faster running. When the flag switch was in the up position, weak field was automatically entered after the full parallel position of the motors had been reached.

The driving motor cars were provided with a 5kW motor generator which converted the 600V traction supply to a 50V dc supply for all control requirements and to provide low-voltage car lighting. This arrangement made the car lighting almost independent of the current rail gaps. The supply from the generator floated across a 48V, 56A/hr lead-acid battery under the control of a voltage regulator. The battery provided a separate feed for emergency lights and the more important control circuits, which therefore remained available even when the motor generator set was not working.

At the outer ends of the driving motors were fitted automatic couplers which carried both air and electric connections in addition to the mechanical coupling. These Wedglock couplers effected instantaneous coupling of the mechanical, electrical and pneumatic connections. Uncoupling was achieved by the touch of a button and coupling was completed similarly after driving one position up to the other. The coupler was of course handed, being different for an 'A' or 'D' end, but it was only the electrical circuits which could not be properly married when 'A'-to-'A' or 'D'-to-'D' couplers came together.

There was an added complication — the 'A' end of all cars carried a solid buffer while the 'D' end had a spring buffer, these two together forming the buffing movement required between every car. The automatic coupling positions also had this arrangement, but the spring buffer extended beyond the coupler face of the Wedglock coupler so that it was not possible to couple two 'D' ends directly together. To overcome this problem when trains got turned (which they regularly did on the Northern Line because of the Kennington Loop) a 'D'-to-'D' coupling adaptor was provided so that a wrong-way train could couple to a right-way train at the 'D' ends. The solid buffers at the 'A' ends, however, did not prevent the Wedglock coupler faces coming together. All units were provided with 'D'-to-'D' coupling adaptors. During the time the 1938 Tube stock was being introduced to the Northern Line the units also had to carry a Wedglock to Ward coupling adaptor, to enable emergency coupling to a Pre-1938 Tube stock train.

The cars of each unit were connected together semi-permanently by fishtail coupling bars carrying four sets of 10-core cables and two pipes for compressed air. A total of 40 separate wires therefore passed from end to end of each unit but only a total of 32 separate circuits were required to pass through the Wedglock couplers, 30 being train wires and two being needed to operate the coupler controls. In accordance with tube rolling stock practice, 600V power lines did not pass between cars, although some local 600V circuits were arranged to pass from the motor cars to adjacent trailer cars for feeding the passenger saloon heaters and to provide limited power for operation of the air compressors which were carried on both the trailer and non-driving motor cars. The compressor provided originally was the rotary KLL4-type which had a 600V dc driving motor.

Each car was provided with two 4ft 6in (1.372m) double doorways on each side, and one 2ft 3in (686mm) doorway at each end on each side except where a driver's cab was provided. All the doors were pneumatically operated under the control of the guard, who normally travelled on the end passenger gangway of the last motor car where door control panels were provided. Each driving motor car had door controls on the end partitions. The control circuit was so arranged that in an emergency the guard could operate with safety from any door panel in the train. The control panels were inoperative if the guard's position switch key was not in position. This practice allowed more flexibility than the arrangement previously provided on the Standard stock. Each panel contained two control buttons, one for normal use which opened all doors and one to energise the 'passenger open' wire. The selection of this latter button did not open the doors but permitted the passengers themselves to open the single or double doors where they were standing by means of push buttons placed both on the outside and inside of the cars, adjacent to the doorways.

The door control circuit was powered from the 50V dc control supply and incorporated the basic safety feature of individual interlocking of sliding doors so that the starting bell could not be given until all the doors were fully closed. The 'passenger open' door control circuit gave a great deal of trouble initially, and several modifications and additional safeguards had to be incorporated to avoid all the possibilities of any door opening in the tunnels while the train was in motion. Subsequently the passenger control feature had to be withdrawn under the blackout conditions of World War 2 but was reintroduced after the war. This passenger amenity was then considered to have such a limited value in proportion to the very heavy maintenance costs incurred that the facility was then withdrawn altogether. The 'passenger open' buttons on the car sides were removed when the cars subsequently passed through Acton Works for overhaul.

The first 1938 Tube stock train ran on the Bakerloo Line on 21 January 1939. Subsequently the whole batch of '58' trailers was transferred to the Bakerloo Line, mostly in three-car units, because the Bakerloo service was confined to six-car trains until after the opening of the junction with the Metropolitan Line at Finchley Road and the extension of Bakerloo Line trains to Stanmore on 20 November 1939. The Bakerloo trains were then increased to seven-car length by the insertion of a non-driving motor car into the even-numbered units.

Prior to the joining of the Bakerloo Line with the Metropolitan, Bakerloo cars had to be transferred to Acton Works or to other Underground lines by way of Willesden Junction and Earls Court. This movement involved two reversals, so the Bakerloo trains normally ran with the 'A' end south (whereas the Northern Line normally ran with the 'A' end north) in order that the 'A' ends would face the west when transferred to Acton Works. On completion of the link with the Metropolitan, transfer of stock then took place via Rayners Lane, which caused the 'A' end to face south, providing a wrong-way train. Following transfer of the maintenance from London Road depot to Neasden depot the whole of the Bakerloo Line fleet was sent round the Watford-Rickmansworth triangle during one weekend to turn it so that the 'A' cars would again face north.

The original plan for the Bakerloo Line arising out of the 1935/40 New Works Programme was for the Bakerloo Line service to be provided from 24 seven-car trains of Standard stock and 23 seven-car trains of 1938 Tube stock, but by June 1945 there were actually 30 seven-car 1938 Tube stock trains and all the '58' trailers on the Bakerloo Line. As the full extent of the Northern Line extensions were not being completed, further 1938 Tube stock trains became available for transfer to the Bakerloo Line so that by 1948 only three seven-car trains of Standard Tube stock were required to make up the service. (How this was achieved is part of the

*Below:*
**A 1938 Tube stock train on the Bakerloo Line in 1981, almost at the end of its running life. Note the roundels instead of the 'London Transport' fleet name, and small white numerals instead of gold leaf for fleet numbers.** *Les Bertram*

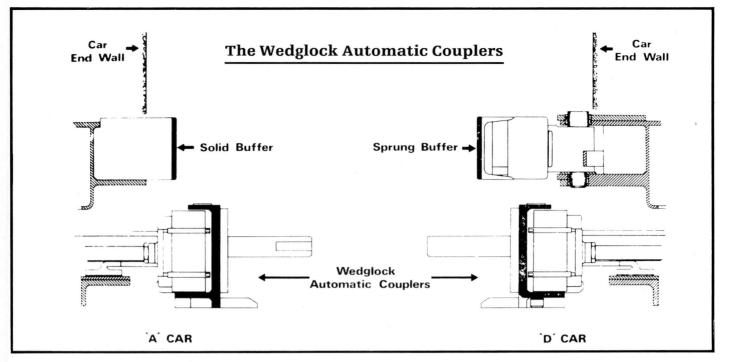

# The Wedglock Automatic Couplers

Car End Wall →

← Solid Buffer

Sprung Buffer →

Car ← End Wall

← Wedglock Automatic Couplers →

`A` CAR

`D` CAR

*Top:*
**A diagrammatic representation of the 'A' and 'D' ends of cars carrying the Wedglock coupler.**

*Above:*
**The experimental conversion of 10306, the precursor of the changes which resulted in the high windows eventually provided in the 1967 Tube stock.**

nine-car train story told in the next chapter.) Subsequently all the Bakerloo Line trains became 1938 Tube stock. Very much later the scrapping of all 1938 Tube stock was arranged to take place through Neasden depot so that the best cars could be selected for retention and further service on that line.

The scrapping of 1938 Tube stock began when the first of the 1972 Mk I Tube stock commenced working on the Northern Line in June 1972. The scrapping continued through the delivery of the 1972 Mk II Tube stock and the 1973 Tube stock until only 36 trains of this type remained to work the Bakerloo Line service. Arrangements were made for the best 36 trains to receive a special overhaul as they passed through Acton Works, which included the fitting of some improvements. One of the important modifications was the fitting of door indicator lights to each car to assist the guard in the location of doors not fully closed, so that improved station working would be achieved.

British Railways' transfer of the cars from Neasden depot to the dealers for scrapping became very difficult, so that arrangements were made to transfer each of the rakes of scrap cars from Neasden to Ruislip depot by battery locomotive, utilising the spur connection built in 1972 between the Uxbridge Line and Ruislip depot to assist the movement of ballast trains over the system. This process continued until the opening of the Jubilee Line when only 36 trains of 1938 Tube stock, retained for the Bakerloo Line, remained. It had originally been agreed that 34 trains would receive an extra-heavy overhaul to prolong their operational life, but subsequently two additional trains were added to the fleet

due to the inferior reliability performance of the trains in service.

A new rolling stock depot was built at Stonebridge Park and brought into service to meet the opening of the Jubilee Line, when it was no longer convenient to transfer the remaining Bakerloo Line trains to Neasden depot for maintenance. Thus the newest rolling stock depot became responsible for maintaining the oldest tube stock then in service, stock which had in fact operated on most of the tube lines at one time or another in its long working career. In addition, four-car units from the Bakerloo Line fleet of 1938 Tube stock operated on the East London Line from January 1974 to June 1977, a service which had previously been the

preserve of surface line rolling stock. Adjustments to track levels had to be made to enable a compromise platform height to be established so that the step down to tube stock floor level was not excessive. Furthermore, from November 1957 to June 1960 unit 10177 operated on the Central Line between Epping and Ongar as one of the shuttle trains. This unit was loaned to the Central Line while the 1935 stock two-car units were withdrawn for alteration and extension into three-car sets by the insertion of trailer cars. It was originally intended that this would be achieved by the purchase of three additional 1938 Tube stock trailers but these were absorbed in the 1949 Tube stock fleet increase and three Standard

81

Tube stock trailers of 1927 construction were converted for the purpose. They were fitted with 'passenger open' door control but no compressors, as these were already fitted to the 'D' motor cars of the unit. The cars converted were originally numbered 7510-12 and were renumbered 70510-12. The first unit including a trailer entered service on the Epping-Ongar route in May 1960. Subsequently these trailers were equipped with de-icing equipment in 1964 but the entire fleet were withdrawn from service by 1969. The 1938 Tube stock in general was not suitable for working on the Central Line round the sharp curves between Shepherd's Bush and White City without modification either to the cars or the tunnels.

The last trains of 1938 Tube stock ran on the Piccadilly Line in December 1975, while all the 1938 Tube stock were withdrawn from regular passenger service on the Northern Line on 14 April 1978, after almost 40 years of continuous service on the line.

In the beginning of the electric service to Watford in April 1917, the Bakerloo trains provided the all-day service with the London & North Western Railway trains providing the additional peak service. This type of service continued with the introduction of the Joint stock which was fully operational by May 1921. However, on 14 June 1965 the regular service of Bakerloo trains beyond Queens Park was withdrawn. The 10 trains stabled at Croxley Green depot were reduced to six working southbound through trains in the morning and northbound in the evening. This group of trains — which only completed one trip to and from Watford daily — was reduced to four from 11 October 1965, and then in September 1982 the trains to and from Watford were withdrawn completely. This reduction in the number of trains enabled six to be withdrawn from the fleet of trains required to maintain the Bakerloo Line service, which was now reduced to 30.

Following the general service reductions imposed following the loss of traffic in December 1982 it became possible to reshuffle the rolling stock between lines so 15 trains of 1959 Tube stock were transferred from the Northern Line to the Bakerloo Line. This in turn enabled in 1983 a further 14 trains of 1938 Tube stock to be withdrawn, leaving only 16 working in passenger service on the Bakerloo. This final group of 1938 Tube stock was then taken out of service as the 1983 Tube stock entered service on the Jubilee Line by a further shuffle of rolling stock between lines, until the whole Bakerloo Line service was being maintained by a fleet of 31 trains of 1959 Tube stock.

At this time, it was thought to be the end of the long and successful life of 1938 Tube stock trains on Underground service. One train was specially refurbished as near as possible to the

*Top:*
**1938 Tube stock as retained in later years for service on the Bakerloo Line. It is carrying roundels instead of 'London Transport' on the side.** *Brian Hardy*

*Above:*
**A display of the development of Tube stock hand grips. The original 1938 Tube stock ones were made of moulded rubber with a wire insert which proved vulnerable to vandalism. They were replaced by a spring type with 'gear lever' knob and chain insert.** *LRT U34850*

original condition of the stock when it entered service in 1938, and it operated the last official passenger run and work specials in honour of the end of 1938 Tube stock. This refurbished train became known as the 'Starlight Express' because of the special adverts carried inside the cars. This restored train entered service on the Bakerloo Line on 3 December 1984 and was available to make the last official service run on 20 November 1985.

An upsurge in traffic required that the service cuts of 1982 should be restored and the need to provide a float of rolling stock to enable the modern tube trains to be converted to OPO (one-person operation) caused five trains of 1938 Tube stock to be saved from the scrap merchants and for them all to be refurbished similar to the 'Starlight Express'. This work was carried out at Ruislip depot, and two of these renovated trains — which had now been equipped with train radios and positive train identification equipment — re-entered service on the Northern Line on the morning of 15 September 1986. These 1938 Tube stock trains will probably therefore remain in service for at least a further two years until some new trains can be constructed. In addition, some 1938 Tube stock cars have been converted for other duties, including personnel carriers for use on the service stock fleet which will undoubtedly outlast the passenger service fleet.

# 14.   The Nine-Car Train Experiment

In the mid-1930s there was considerable criticism about overcrowding on tube lines, especially on the Northern Line, so consideration was given to operating longer trains. It was relatively simple for station platforms between Golders Green and Colindale to be lengthened to accommodate trains of nine-car length as these stations were in the open and thus did not involve heavy engineering.

At first an eight-car test took place in August 1937 when a Standard stock tube train was made up into the formation CT-M-M-T-T-M-M-CT (that is with control trailers at the leading or driving ends). This train was operated between Edgware and Kennington, running round the loop to return. The tests indicated that it would be possible to run a nine-car train provided certain precautions were taken.

The stations at Burnt Oak, Colindale, Hendon Central, Brent and Golders Green could accommodate nine cars but at Edgware (a terminal station) the leading two cars were off the platform. Tunnel stations could not accommodate more than seven cars, so it was arranged in the southbound direction that at Hampstead, Belsize Park and Camden Town the trailing two cars remained in the tunnel at the station stops, but after Camden Town the leading two cars stopped in the tunnel, except at Tottenham Court Road. In the northbound direction the rear two cars called at the platforms between Kennington and Leicester Square while from Tottenham Court Road to Hampstead the front two cars were accommodated in the platforms.

The train formation of Standard tube stock nine-car trains was M-T-M-CT-T-CT-M-T-M, and two trains of this formation began operating in passenger service between Colindale (where the reversing siding had been lengthened to take nine cars) and Kennington Loop by way of Charing Cross. The middle motor cars were fitted with special switching controls to cut out the doors on the two leading and two trailing cars as required to cover the working arrangements. Extra control

lines and a special roof switch box on the guard's gangway of these cars were provided. The guard actually rode at the guard's end of the inner-position motor cars which were fitted with special door cut-out switches.

The operation was considered successful and four workings for nine-car stock were arranged in the timetable, so from February 1938 until the outbreak of World War 2 some nine-car trains operated between Edgware (where platform 1 was altered to take such a train length) and Kennington. Also, provision was made in the order for 1938 Tube stock for 90 special cars to be constructed to enable 10 nine-car trains to be provided. These cars were delivered towards the end of the programme because of the difficult door control requirements and the order consisted of a number of special cars — in fact each car of each train was numbered 1 to 9 as they had to be formed up in this order. In particular, a new type of car, the 'special non-driving motor' car, was born. Because the nine-car train formation was virtually a block train with driving positions at the outer ends only, a special car was necessary to allow the train to be divided intermediately and to provide the door controls at a point which would always be in the station's platform, whichever two cars were left in the tunnel. Many sidings and track sections on the Northern Line accommodated only seven cars, so it was necessary in an emergency to arrange for two cars to be easily uncoupled from either end.

Cars 1 and 9 were driving motor cars, No 1 being an 'A' car and No 9 being the 'D' car. These cars were almost standard 1938 Tube stock motor cars, being provided with a motor generator set, but they were not fitted with guards' control panels at the end gangways.

Cars 2 and 8 were semi-permanently coupled to the 1 and 9 cars and were non-driving motor cars. They were provided with a Ward-type mechanical coupler at the opposite end to the semi-permanent coupler. The electrical and pneumatic connections were made at the Ward coupling end in a similar

fashion to that previously used on the Standard Tube stock with jumper cables. This arrangement made emergency uncoupling easy for operating staff. These cars were also fitted with KLL4-type rotary compressors.

Cars 3 and 7 were the special non-driving motor cars: the main reason for the label 'special' was that they were equipped with a motor generator set instead of a compressor which a non-driving motor car normally carried. In addition, these cars were provided with a guard's control panel, a handbrake which could be applied by the guard, and a fault isolating switch which could divide the vulnerable circuits of the train into two separate sections. These cars too had Ward couplings and attachments for making the electrical and pneumatic connections to the 2 and 8 cars at the appropriate ends.

Cars 4 and 6 were trailer cars, the only trailer cars in the formation. Carrying compressors, they were in fact normal trailer cars except for one small feature — the electrical feeds for lighting and operating the compressor were taken from the opposite end of the car to normal.

Car 5, the centre car, was the only 'normal' car in the formation, being a standard non-driving motor car.

By June 1939 two of the four nine-car workings in the timetable were being operated by 1938 tube nine-car stock, but the arrangement lasted for a very short time as the start of World War 2 caused this type of operation to be abandoned.

The nine-car rolling stock was then made up into block seven-car trains with the formation 1-2x3-5-7x8-9, the guard riding on cars 3 or 7, the special non-driving motor cars. The cars which were withdrawn from the nine-car trains were the trailer cars; and to compensate in power requirements, cars 5 and 8 had the traction motors removed, virtually converting them into trailer cars. Uncoupling in an emergency was still arranged between cars 2 and 3, and 7 and 8.

These seven-car block trains con-

tinued to operate on the Northern Line in special workings where uncoupling was not required, but following the outbreak of war uncoupling of trains was abandoned in any case. After the cessation of hostilities the uncoupling arrangements were restored but subsequently an investigation of the economics of uncoupling indicated that it was very doubtful if there was any financial advantage in running more frequent shorter trains against the cost of providing the uncoupling service, and in spite of some reduction in car miles that might be possible. Uncoupling of trains in the off-peak was discontinued on tube lines during 1960/61 but continued for a time on the Northern & City Line until 1964, where two-car trains composed of a motor car and control trailer were operated during the off-peak periods.

When seven-car trains were uncoupled it was the normal practice to

*Above:*
**A nine-car train of Standard stock at Golders Green, with the guard leaning from his operating position at the seventh car of the train.** *LRT U24609*

*Below:*
**A northbound 7-car train of 1938 Tube stock climbs out of the tunnel and approaches Queen's Park.** *R. G. Bradford*

run the four-car in service and stable the three-car position. On the Northern Line however a three-car portion was considered adequate for operation on the 'City' side services in the off-peak. Following a number of failures of three-car units caused by loss of air following the failure of the single KLL4-type compressor carried on the trailer car, arrangements were then made for the 69 three-car standard units on the Northern Line to be fitted with two compressors. In order that these units — which could be operated

singly in passenger service — could be recognised easily, a 'C' was placed adjacent to the trailer car number.

The guard on the seven-car block trains had to ride two cars forward of the rear because the leading driving motor cars were not altered to provide a guard's position, which then remained on the No 3 and No 7 type cars. The special remotely-operated end door cut-out arrangements used on the nine-car formations were still utilised when necessary on the seven-car block formations.

# 15.  1949 Tube Stock

In 1948 proposals were made for the extension of the Bakerloo from Elephant & Castle to Camberwell, and additional rolling stock was ordered from the Birmingham Railway Carriage & Wagon Co to provide the additional trains required. Complete trains were not ordered — instead only 70 non-driving motor cars of a new design, together with 21 trailers — because at this time there were still three trains of Pre-1938 Tube stock seven-car formation still operating on the Bakerloo Line and there were in store the trailer cars released from the nine-car train stock when they were reduced to seven-car block trains. There were also the three six-car trains of 1935 Experimental stock — the streamlined version — which had been withdrawn from service and stored during the war years. The order for the 91 new cars took the availability of these cars into account.

Before the purchase of the 1949 Tube stock, the fleet of 1938 Tube stock consisted of 1,179 vehicles, including the '58' trailers converted from the 1927 Standard stock. This fleet was then augmented by the addition of the 91 new cars together with 18 of the 1935 Experimental stock (streamlined cars) which were converted at Acton Works to trailer cars to make a total of 1,288 cars, which could then be made up into 184 seven-car trains.

This fleet was subsequently allocated 54 for the Bakerloo, 115 for the Northern, and 15 for the Piccadilly Line when the proposed Camberwell extension scheme was abandoned. The Bakerloo and Piccadilly allocations enabled more Pre-1938 Tube stock to be transferred to the Central Line for the lengthening of a further number of seven-car trains to eight cars. All the 1938 Tube stock trains however were not now identical. The operation of the block seven-car trains derived from the nine-car stock had encouraged the view that driving motor cars in the middle were both a waste of capital equipment furnishing the cabs, a loss of passenger space and unnecessary without uncoupling. Operating and engineering flexibility, exceedingly difficult to

justify in financial terms, could therefore be sacrificed by the provision of a new type of car called the uncoupling non-driving motor car. As such a car was to take the place of a normal driving motor car, a motor generator set had to be fitted in place of the compressor, making it similar to the 'special' non-driving motor cars provided for the nine-car formation.

Although 70 uncoupling non-driving motor cars were purchased new, actually 92 were required: 46 'A' end cars and 46 'D' end cars. All the 'D' end cars were purchased new, but 22 of the 'A' end cars were converted from existing non-driving motor cars. All 20 of the special non-driving motor cars from the nine-car stock were selected for conversion together with two other normal non-driving motor cars. Most of the conversion work was undertaken at Acton Works but the new motor cars were delivered to Ealing Common depot where they were prepared for service. The 24 'A' end uncoupling non-driving motor cars were then transferred to Morden depot while the 46 'D' end cars were sent to Neasden for operation on the Bakerloo Line.

The uncoupling non-driving motor cars were fitted with Wedglock automatic couplers to enable coupling to normal four-car units of 1938 Tube stock. These uncoupling non-driving motor cars were invariably made up on the inward end of the three-car portion so that 46 east- and 46 west-facing three-car portions were provided in this way.

A handbrake which had a special locking device to avoid interference by passengers was provided. In addition, a cabinet opened by a key containing a shunting controller was fitted to the end bulkhead, enabling the three-car portion to be moved into and out of service during the uncoupling periods. Tripcocks were also fitted so that shunting over main line tracks could be accomplished safely. The shunter was required to drive keeping observation through the communicating door which therefore provided only limited vision. This arrangement caused staff difficulties so that it was July 1952

before these cars were accepted for service in the way they were intended, although the first car of this type had entered service in November 1951.

All the units with 'D' end uncoupling cars were allocated to the Bakerloo Line, and while this type of car was reasonably satisfactory for shunting between the uncoupling station and an adjacent siding, conditions at Watford Junction were such that the uncoupled unit had to be transferred to Croxley Green sheds, a considerable distance over main line trackage from the uncoupling point. This movement was found to be somewhat difficult with the restricted view through the communicating door and trains scheduled to uncouple at Watford had to be made up with standard three-car units with standard driving motor cars at both ends. Arrangements were therefore made for the 15 trains allocated to the Piccadilly Line to be made up with 'D' end uncoupling non-driving motors, in order to release an equivalent number of normal three-car units for uncoupling at Watford. This change produced a further complication because Piccadilly trains normally had the three-car portion at the east or 'D' end, but with 'D' uncoupling cars the three-car portion was now at the wrong end because it had to be coupled on what was normally the west end of the train. This problem was then overcome by completely turning the trains so that the 1938 Tube stock on the Piccadilly Line then faced the wrong way. This turning was achieved by running all the trains, over one weekend, to High Street Kensington and back to South Kensington. When this was done the three-car portion was now at the east end of the trains. When general uncoupling was subsequently abandoned on the Piccadilly Line the trains were again turned to be right way round.

The reduction of the nine-car trains to seven-car blocks had produced 20 spare trailer cars, and there were in addition six trailer cars stored since the war years, three being purchased to expand three of the 1935 Experimental stock units to three-car units which were never used for this purpose. It was

*Above:*
**A 1949 Tube stock motor bogie of improved design, with welded side frames riveted to cross members.** *LRT 3451/2*

decided to utilise these spare cars to increase the number of trains of 1938 Tube stock by expanding the block train principle by the rearrangement of cars. The spare trailers released the special non-driving motor cars, allowing them to be converted to uncoupling non-driving motor cars, and also those non-driving motor cars that had been acting as trailers in the block formations with the motors removed, allowing these to revert to their proper function as non-driving motor cars. Following this rearrangement there were three types of block train.

There were six trains of Type 1, which had the formation 1-2x3-T-7x8-9. These trains continued to operate as previously with Ward couplings between cars 2 and 3 and 7 and 8, with the guard riding on cars 3 and 7, where the door control panels were provided.

Type 2 trains, of which there were four, had the formation 1-2x3-4-5-6-9, reinstating the No 4 and No 6 trailer cars which had been removed from the nine-car formation originally. The No 5 car had been restored as a non-driving motor car. At the 'A' end of the train the guard still rode on the special non-driving motor car, the No 3 car, while at the 'D' end the nine-car motor car had been converted to standard with a guard's control panel placed on the trailing gangway.

Four Type 3 block trains had the formation 'A'-4-5-5-7x8-'D', where the leading cars were normal 'A' and 'D' end driving motor cars. The No 4 car was a renovated nine-car trailer, and while the No 5 cars were restored as normal non-driving motor cars, these

were not enough to complete all four trains, and one normal non-driving motor car which had been stored was also used to make up the number.

There were now 14 block trains, 10 on the Northern and four on the Bakerloo. This arrangement did not last very long because delivery of the 1949 Tube stock required further re-formations and alteration to the rolling stock. All the special non-driving motor cars were converted to uncoupling non-driving motors and standardised, except that the Ward couplers and hose connections were replaced by a Wedglock coupler arrangement. Some of these cars had to be physically turned since they all became 'A' end uncoupling cars. All the other '9' stock was converted to standard and the numeral 9 in the number became 1. Care had been taken originally to number the cars in the same series but with the prefix number 9 instead of 1. The uncoupling non-driving motor cars however were provided with a new numerical series beginning with 30000, retaining the convention of even numbers being 'A' end cars and odd numbers 'D' end cars. The converted cars took the earlier numbers.

The original allocation after the completion of the work was: the Bakerloo Line had 54 seven-car trains with 46 having 'D' end uncoupling non-driving motor cars; the Northern Line had 115 seven-car trains, with 69 normal train sets with the three-car unit at the 'D' end, leaving the remainder as 46 trains with 'D' end units having uncoupling non-driving motors; and the Piccadilly Line also had three-car units at the 'D' end on a

normal train formation. Subsequently, the 15 trains on the Piccadilly Line were changed over with uncoupling non-driving motor trains from the Bakerloo, as already described.

The 'A' end and 'D' end driving motor cars were always used in pairs, the 10xxx and the 11xxx numbers matching. Odd numbers were used for three-car units and even numbers for four-car ones. The introduction of the uncoupling non-driving motors meant that this simple arrangement was upset as some of the driving motors from three-car units would require to be made up into four-car units subsequently, but it was decided not to renumber any cars, and four-car units using odd numbered pairs were chosen at the end of the series and therefore started at 10289 and 11289, rising to 10333 and 11333.

During October and November 1966, 1938 Tube stock was introduced to the Northern & City Line, and Drayton Park ceased to be a general maintenance depot because the units were then changed over regularly with Golders Green depot.

Battery locomotives were used to transfer the units to and from Highgate depot, from where they were generally transferred to and from Golders Green depot under their own power. This arrangement continued until 29 September 1970 when the maintenance of the track between Highgate and Finsbury Park became too expensive. Thereafter the transfer of 1938 Tube stock units was made to and from Neasden. This was a much more extensive operation, necessitating running by way of King's Cross, Eastern Region and the City Widened Lines to the Circle Line, and then over the Metropolitan Line to Neasden depot.

The units now used to work the Northern & City had to be allocated on a semi-permanent basis because they could not carry Bakerloo Line diagrams, having to be equipped with Northern Line diagrams. These transfers, utilising battery locomotives, took place on a regular basis and involved the use of a pilotman between King's Cross and Finsbury Park.

This arrangement continued until 1975. On 6 September 1975, Northern & City passenger trains ceased to work into Moorgate but a service continued between Drayton Park and Old Street until 4 October 1975, when the line was taken over completely by British Railways and London Transport rolling stock withdrawn.

Unfortunately, on 28 February 1975, only a few months before these trains were to be withdrawn from service, a six-car train of 1938 Tube stock was driven at full speed through the terminal station at Moorgate into the short dead-end tunnel beyond the platform, resulting in serious loss of life. It was the worst accident in the history of London's Underground.

# 16.  1956/59 Tube Stock

Traffic continued to increase on both the Central and the Piccadilly Lines, and to provide additional capacity without involving costly civil engineering it became necessary to plan for the replacement of the Pre-1938 Tube stock which, in addition to having a limited capacity because of the space occupied by the switch compartment, was becoming unreliable and somewhat expensive to maintain. It was decided therefore to order three prototype trains, one from each of three different car builders: Metropolitan-Cammell, Birmingham Railway Carriage & Wagon Co and the Gloucester Railway Carriage & Wagon Co.

Each train consisted of seven cars comprising semi-permanently coupled three- and four-car units in the formation M-T-NDM-M × M-T-M.

The designs incorporated three major innovations for tube stock, although the general arrangement followed very closely the 1938/49 Tube stock. The bodies had external cladding of unpainted aluminium; the bogies were provided with rubber suspension instead of steel springs (a change which eliminated a large number of wearing parts); and finally the car illumination was greatly improved by the installation of fluorescent lighting in the passenger saloons. A return was made to the roller destination blind over the front cab door, which had first been tried on the earlier cars of the Pre-1938 Tube stock, illuminated this time by a fluorescent tube.

The AEI-manufactured PCM-type electrical control equipment provided, however, was only a slightly modified version of that of the 1938 Tube stock which had given good service.

Complete flexibility of the units of the train was not provided, unlike that of the 1938 Tube stock, because the driving motor cars at the outer ends of the train were not fitted with fully automatic couplers. Only mechanical coupling could be arranged for emergency use at the outer end. Subsequently these cars were modified to couple with the subsequent 1959 Tube stock for which they were in all respects the prototypes.

The EP brake with retardation control and self-lapping brake controller — similar but not identical to that fitted to 1938 Tube stock — was standard equipment, but the motor generator set had an additional armature to provide the alternating current required for the fluorescent lighting. This arrangement was designed to avoid the magnetic hum produced by the 'R' stock motor generator sets providing ac for fluorescent lighting. This new machine supplied alternating current at 110V 850 hertz (cycles per second) for the fluorescent lighting. This high frequency was chosen to avoid interference with external signalling equipment in case of a fault developing.

The traction master controller was provided with three positions — shunt, series and parallel. The shunting position allowed slow running in the yards and depots with resistances connected in series with the motors, while the series position provided all the accelerating steps up to the point where the two motors on each motor car were connected together in series across the 600V, giving a speed of up to 15mph. The parallel position enabled acceleration to full speed. Higher speeds could be attained by operating the weak field flag switch. The flag was placed in such a position in the cab that when it was cut in it could be observed external to the train, as the higher speed was only permitted on the outer sections of the lines.

The first of the prototype trains entered service on the Piccadilly Line on 9 September 1957 and all three were in service by April 1958. The provision of these three trains enabled further cars of Pre-1938 Tube stock to be released for operation on the Central Line. The trials with the three trains were successful and orders were placed

*Below:*
**A 1959 Tube stock train.**  *LRT 1847/5*

for 76 seven-car trains of what became known as 1959 Tube stock from Metropolitan-Cammell Ltd, to replace the Pre-1938 Tube stock on the Piccadilly Line, allowing all the Pre-1938 Tube stock trains on the Central Line to be increased to an eight-car formation. This proposal had the merit of obtaining immediate benefit for the Piccadilly Line by providing all the trains with the same passenger capacity as the small number of 1938 Tube stock already working on the line. It also provided some time for the development of new rolling stock to meet the requirements of the Central Line to replace the Pre-1938 Tube stock working on that line.

The 76 new trains of 1959 Tube stock were virtually identical to 1956 Tube stock. One visual difference concerned the frontal appearance: the 1956 motor cars had the five-aspect marker light arrangement used on the 1938 Tube stock, but, as destination lights were now no longer an operating requirement, the 1959 Tube stock cars were provided only with twin headlights in place of the marker light cabinet.

It was subsequently realised that the detailed development of a new type of motor car for the Central Line would take too long, and, as serious complaints regarding the reliability and overcrowding on the Central Line were arising, a change in the proposals was made, so that after the nineteenth 1959 Tube stock had entered service on the Piccadilly Line the remainder of this stock began working on the Central Line.

The first seven-car train of 1959 Tube stock entered passenger service on the Piccadilly Line on 14 December 1959 while the twentieth train of the delivery began working on the Central Line in July 1960. The last of the 1959 Tube stock vehicles went into service on the Central Line on 30 March 1962, but were later transferred to the Piccadilly Line, so that by June 1964 all 76 trains of 1959 Tube stock were working on this line.

Following the purchase and introduction of the 1973 Tube stock to the Piccadilly Line, all the 1959 Tube stock together with the three prototype 1956 Tube stock trains were transferred to the Northern Line. The 1959 Tube stock first entered service on the Northern Line on 1 December 1975 and last ran on the Piccadilly Line on 5 October 1979. This stock then became the mainstay of the Northern Line service.

Following the opening of the Jubilee Line on 1 May 1979, the truncated Bakerloo and the new Jubilee Line (taking over the Stanmore section) were operated as separate railways. The 1938 Tube stock operated on the Bakerloo with Stonebridge Park as the maintenance depot, and the 1972 Tube stock Mk II on the Jubilee Line, based at Neasden depot. Subsequently, the Bakerloo Line service to Watford was

*Above:*
**An interior view of a 1959/62 Tube stock car.**  *LRT 15307*

*Bottom:*
**A 1959/62 Tube stock motor bogie.**  *LRT L7112*

withdrawn from 24 September 1982, after which Bakerloo trains only carried passengers as far as Stonebridge Park. The withdrawal north of Stonebridge Park reduced the number of stations served by London Transport trains from 277 to 266, marking the abandonment of 65 years of Bakerloo train service. Bakerloo trains began operating again to Harrow & Weald-

# Some 1938 and 1959/62 Tube Stock Train Formations

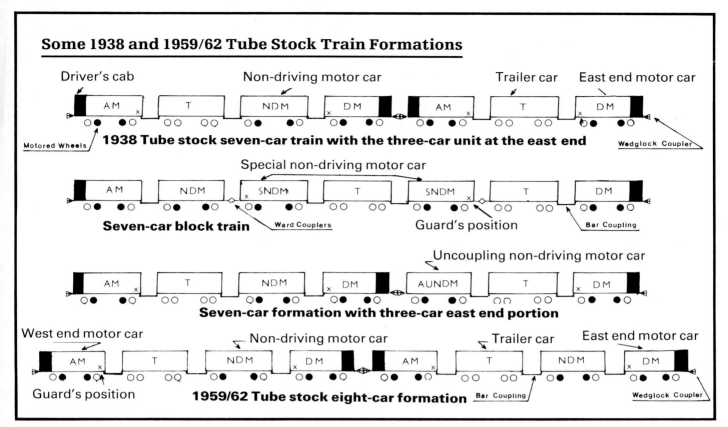

**1938 Tube stock seven-car train with the three-car unit at the east end**

**Seven-car block train**

**Seven-car formation with three-car east end portion**

**1959/62 Tube stock eight-car formation**

stone during peak hours on 4 June 1984; when the negative rail, which had not been used for about 18 months, had to be specially cleaned — a battery locomotive was used to achieve this.

Following these changes it was decided to reduce the 1938 Tube stock to a minimum and finally to withdraw this stock altogether. As part of this process a 1959 Tube stock train was transferred to Stonebridge Park on 5 December 1982. To match the 1938 Tube stock formation the 1959 Tube stock was formed into three-car (north) and four-car (south) units. Finally, after the initial withdrawal of all the 1938 Tube stock, the total service on the Bakerloo Line was provided by seven-car 1959 Tube stock trains.

The 1959 Tube stock followed the pattern of the 1956 Tube stock in almost all aspects. Wedglock automatic couplers, however, were provided at both ends of all units, whether they were formed of three or four cars following the pattern of the 1938 Tube stock. The four-car unit had a non-driving motor car, but unlike the 1938 Tube stock sets this car did not carry a compressor. The trailer cars, whether in three- or four-car units, were each fitted with two compressors, providing a train with a total free air capacity of 620cu ft/min. The compressors themselves were of a two-stage reciprocating type specially designed to fit in the restricted space underneath the floor of a tube car. One of the most difficult design features of the 1938 Tube stock had been the provision of a suitable compressor to fit under the car floor. A high-speed two-stage rotary

compressor had been installed on this stock, and, although less noisy than a reciprocating type, had proved expensive in maintenance, so it was necessary to replace this design and in addition to provide two on the three-car units to enable them to work in service alone. An interesting feature of the provision of two compressors on the trailer cars was that each one received its power feed from a different driving motor car, one from each end of the unit.

Since no passenger control of individual doors was provided, the air door equipment was simplified so that only one set of operating valves was required for all doors on one side of each car. By this means the equipment was simplified to give extra reliability. However, the major innovation on these tube stock trains was the provision of door fault indicator lights mounted outside each car which indicated to the station staff the cars on which doors had not closed properly, making for additional operating reliability.

The traction motors and control were virtually identical with that provided on the 1956 Tube stock; so also were the bogies, with rubber suspension instead of steel springs. The bogies followed the practice introduced with the 1935 Experimental stock and 1938 Tube stock of having only one traction motor on each motor bogie, mounted on the inner axle carried on a roller suspension sleeve and driving through single-spur gears with a 7° helical. The practice of having helical teeth on the gear wheels was generally introduced on the 1938 Tube stock to reduce the

noise of the gears as they were now directly beneath passenger accommodation and not under a switch compartment.

The LT112-type traction motor on the bogie at the leading end of each driving motor car was fitted with a speedometer generator at the opposite end to the driving pinion, directly connected to a recording instrument in the driver's cab. Originally the 1938 Tube stock had been fitted with a speedometer generator mounted on the truck frame which received magnetic impulses from spigots cast in the motor wheel spokes. These instruments were not sufficiently robust for the hard service required and became a maintenance liability. The new type of speedometer generator for the 1959 Tube stock was fitted only to those motors placed in the leading position in driving motor cars.

The 1956 Tube stock cars were originally numbered in a new series resulting in the three seven-car trains being numbered in the series 40xxx-45xxx-44xxx-43xxx-42xxx-45xxx-41xxx. However, when the 1959 Tube stock was numbered, another, much simpler, numbering scheme was adopted. The first seven-car train of 1959 Tube stock was numbered 1012-2012-9013-1013x1014-2014-1015, with the trailer cars taking the same even number as the 'A' end driving motor to which they were attached plus 1000, while the non-driving motor took the same odd number as the 'D' end driving motor to which it was attached plus 8000. The 1956 Tube stock, after being made operationally interchangeable

*Above left:*
**A 1938 tube stock door track.** *LRT*

*Above right:*
**A 1959/62 Tube stock door track.** *LRT*

with the 1959 Tube stock, was renumbered at the beginning of this series.

Electric door-operating equipment had been used successfully on American subway trains for many years and one of the claims made for such equipment was that it was rarely affected by very cold weather, which sometimes caused unreliable operation with pnuematic door gear. One train of 1959 Tube stock with car numbers 1020-2020-9021-1021x1022-1023 was equipped with electric door operators. With these, the movement of the door engine arms was controlled by an electric motor instead of air-operated engine. The equipment was controlled exactly the same as the pneumatic equipment, so these units with electric door operators could be coupled to units having pneumatic equipment and there was no need to keep the train segregated. In 1976 the electric door gear was replaced by air door equipment.

Unfortunately the 1959 Tube stock did not have good riding properties, especially on the long section between Acton Town and Hammersmith on the Piccadilly Line, and the rubber suspension was modified before the cars were transferred to the Northern Line. This followed the introduction of the 1973 Tube stock to the Piccadilly Line.

A feature added to both the 1959 Tube stock and the subsequent but similar 1962 Tube stock was a built-in battery-fed stabling light to avoid the need to place an oil tail lamp on the end of a train left standing in sidings. Although the two types of stock were generally similar, the stabling lights were fitted on different sides of the twin headlights, because of the slightly different cab layouts, the 1959 Tube stock had the light on the side next to the centre cab door while the 1962 Tube stock had the light to the outside of the twin headlights.

Following the rolling stock transfers made possible by service reductions in December 1982, 15 trains of 1959 Tube stock were transferred from the Northern Line to the Bakerloo. The first train of 1959 Tube stock entered service on the line on 28 February 1983 while

the last train of this group was transferred on 3 October 1983. Subsequently another train was transferred in order to enable the regular passenger service to Harrow & Wealdstone to be restored on 4 June 1984. The release of this train was obtained by the transfer of a 1962 Tube stock train (reduced from eight cars to seven cars) from the Central Line to the Northern Line.

After the introduction of the 15 trains of 1983 Tube stock to the Jubilee Line,

further 1959 Tube stock was transferred from the Northern Line to the Bakerloo Line until the whole service was provided by this stock.

Subsequently another reshuffle of rolling stock was planned with the introduction of OPO, as it was not economic to convert 1959 Tube stock to this form of operation. Arrangements were therefore made for the Bakerloo to be provided with 1972 Tube stock so converted and the 1959 Tube stock returned to the Northern Line.

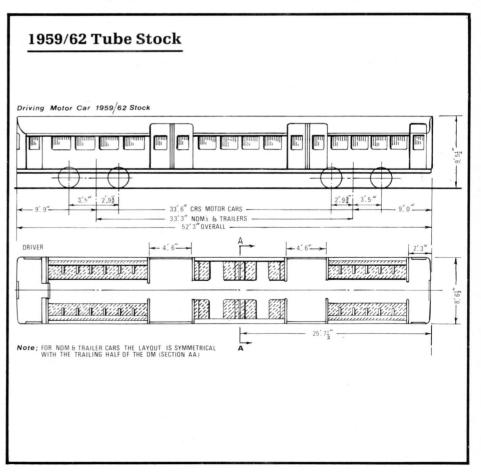

# 17. 1962 Tube Stock

It had originally been intended that the Central Line would be re-equipped with eight-car trains of the 1960 Tube stock arrangement, with new motor cars and refurbished Pre-1938 Tube stock trailers. However, the need for the provision of new rolling stock became urgent because it had become obvious that the Pre-1938 Tube stock had become incapable of bearing the strain of the highly intensive and congested service.

As a first move in the change of plan caused by the problems arising on the Central Line, it was decided that after the nineteenth of the 76 1959 Tube stock trains ordered had begun operating on the Piccadilly Line, this stock should be transferred to the Central Line. As eight-car trains were required on the Central Line, Metropolitan-Cammell was instructed to add 57 additional non-driving motor (NDM) cars to the original order for 532 cars and to adjust the building programme so that one of these NDM cars was delivered with each of the Piccadilly Line seven-car trains after the nineteenth. These additional NDM cars enabled the three-car unit to be increased to a four-car unit and thus the Central Line trains could be made up of two identical four-car units coupled together.

These 57 non-driving motor cars were in fact the first of the 1962 Tube stock of which a total of 676 vehicles were now ordered. The order for this group of stock — less the 57 — went out to competitive tender. Orders for 450 cars were placed with the Birmingham Railway Carriage & Wagon Co, and for 169 cars with British Railways workshops. These latter were in fact all the trailer cars needed to make 84½ eight-car trains to meet the Central Line service. The order placed with the Birmingham Co was made up of 338 driving motor cars and 112 non-driving motor cars. Then, early in 1961, it was announced that the Birmingham Railway Carriage & Wagon Co wished to be relieved of its contract and had agreed to transfer the order to Metropolitan-Cammell. The 1962 Tube stock was therefore delivered virtually as a continuation of the order for 1959 Tube stock.

In February 1962 Metropolitan-Cammell announced the completion of the contract for 589 cars which included the 57 non-driving motor cars of 1962 Tube stock as well as the whole of the 1959 Tube stock cars, and indicated that the production line for the bulk of the 1962 Tube stock would continue uninterrupted.

The 1962 Tube stock was in any case completely compatible with 1959 Tube stock, having the same traction equipment and braking systems. The bogies too were virtually identical in construction and design, and so were the traction motors. The numbering system applied to the 1962 Tube stock started at 1400 for the driving motor cars and 2400 for the trailers; while the non-driving motor cars commenced at 9401, continuing the convention that they should be odd numbers to match the east end driving motor cars with which they were normally associated. The original 57 cars ordered to run initially with the 1959 Tube stock were given numbers late in the series so that they could be re-formed with their matching numbers when these were delivered, without affecting the service provision on the Central Line too much. When these cars were removed from the 1959 Tube stock a seven-car train was then transferred to the Piccadilly.

Subsequently the order was further intended to provide three additional eight-car trains to release the 1960 Tube stock for the Automatic Train Operation (ATO) trials, and one additional three-car unit was also obtained so that a three-car train could be provided on the Aldwych shuttle service instead of retaining special shuttle cars. Later, to improve the stock availability on the Piccadilly Line, three trains of 1962 Tube stock were also transferred from the Central Line; in this case the three non-driving motor cars were stored until these trains were returned to the Central Line.

One of the main differences in the equipment installed on the 1962 Tube stock was the provision of a motor alternator rectifier (MAR) set for the supply of control and auxiliary circuits. This equipment had static regulation, a great improvement on the moving carbon regulator associated with the motor generator set on the 1959 Tube stock. The emergency lighting provision in the passenger saloon was still provided with tungsten filament lamps fed off the battery, the same as 1959 Tube stock, although the 1960 Tube stock had been provided with inverter-fed fluorescent tubes from a similar MAR set.

In general the equipment of the 1962

*Below:*
**The guard's door panels on 1959/62 Tube stock.** *LRT*

Tube stock was almost identical with that of the 1959 Tube stock. Nevertheless the opportunity was taken to incorporate certain refinements which had been found desirable following operating experience with the earlier stock. The driver's brake controllers were fitted with poppet valves instead of the rotary face valves, a change which extensive trials had proved to be of value in reducing maintenance. Another important maintenance-reducing change was the provision of plug-in facilities for all electrically-operated air valves. This arrangement enabled valves to be changed more speedily, especially the door-operating equipment and the brake-operating valves, eliminating the danger of loose or broken connections.

The first 1962 Tube stock train of eight cars began operating on the Central Line on 12 April 1962, and all the trains were available for service by 17 May 1964, when the last of the 1959 Tube stock was returned to the Piccadilly Line as a seven-car train.

Some 30 1959 Tube stock trailer cars — those numbered between 2100 and 2216 in four-car units — and 25 1962 Tube stock trailer cars were fitted with de-icing equipment. In the case of the 1962 Tube stock it was all those with the number 6 as the last number of the set, starting with 2406 and ending with 2646. It should be noted that the trailer cars were all even-numbered, matching the even-numbered west end or 'A' motor cars to which they were attached in the unit formation. The de-icing equipment was controlled by switches in the drivers' cabs.

Unfortunately the floor plates of the 1962 Tube stock trailer cars built by British Railways required some additional attention (which included replacement) at the second overhaul, and it was necessary to retain the cars at Acton Works for extra time for repair. Therefore, after July 1979, units leaving Acton Works were re-formed, which broke the numbering sequence which had been established. Subsequently some renumbering took place to reinstate the sequence.

In 1969, three trains of 1962 Tube stock were transferred from the Central Line to the Piccadilly Line to meet a temporary rolling stock shortage, the eight-car trains being reduced to seven cars and the withdrawn non-driving motor cars temporarily stored. These trains were returned in 1976. Then, during the rearrangements of rolling stock following the 1982 service reductions, three trains of 1962 Tube stock were transferred to the Northern Line to assist in the transfer of 1959 Tube stock to the Bakerloo Line.

The future renovation programme of the Central Line includes the complete re-equipping of the line with new rolling stock and envisages the transfer of most of the 1962 Tube stock to finish its working life on the Northern Line.

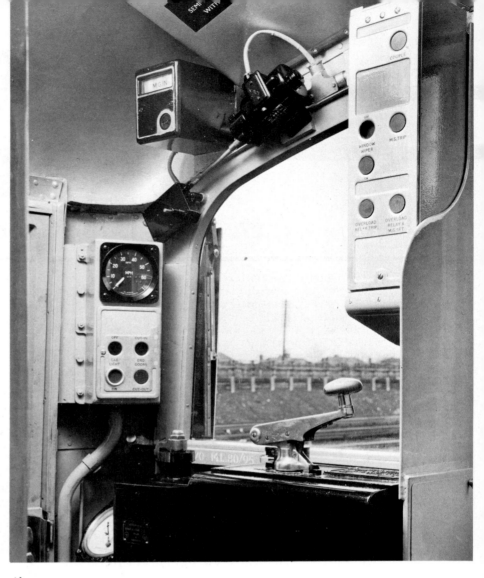

*Above:*
**The driver's controls on 1959/62 Tube stock.**  *LRT*

*Below:*
**A comparison of plug-type and wire connecting-type brake valves on 1959 and 1962 tube stock.**  *LRT*

# 18.  1960 Tube Stock

*Above:*
**1960 tube stock after conversion for ATO working on the Woodford-Hainault shuttle. The cab doors have been sealed up and a tripcock resetting cord provided at the leading cab door. An additional isolating handle to change over from tripcock to automatic trip valve has been provided on the headstock.** *Ian Allan Library*

In anticipation of a large renewal programme for the Pre-1938 Tube stock on the Central Line, 12 prototype motor cars were ordered in 1958. At the same time 12 Pre-1938 Tube stock trailer cars were reconditioned and altered to run with them to form three eight-car trains of a new formation for operation on the Central Line.

The 12 new cars were all driving motor cars of an entirely new design, and for the first time in tube stock formations these motor cars were provided with four traction motors, two on each bogie. The four-car units would be made up into M-T-T-M formation and it was proposed that a further 338 motor cars and 338 reconditioned trailers would be produced, but this plan was never completed for two main reasons: it became necessary to improve the Central Line service much

quicker than this proposal could be achieved; and the conversion work proposed on the trailers proved much more expensive than originally intended, so the whole plan was modified.

The first of these prototype trains entered service on the Central Line on 9 November 1960. Like the 1959 Tube stock the external panels were of unpainted aluminium. The control equipment continued to be of the now well-tried PCM-type manufactured by AEI, modified so that one set now controlled four traction motors instead

of two. Pairs of Type LT113 traction motors were connected in permanent series, providing the normal series-parallel connection of the two series groups on each motor car. An additional piece of safety gear in the form of a wheelspin protection device had now been provided since the two motors operated in permanent series. If one motor of a pair began to overspeed, the line breaker opened and the camshaft of the control equipment returned to the 'off' position, ensuring that the equipment notched up from rest automatically, correcting the wheelspin. The motors were still mounted on axle suspension roller bearing sleeves but the axles were equally disposed from the centre-line because there was now no necessity to put more adhesive weight on a single motored axle.

The eight-car trains were to be formed by coupling two identical units together. Fully automatic coupling was provided at the outer ends of the motor cars, but for the first time in tube stock arrangements the motor cars were not handed but were arranged to be fully reversible so that the motor cars had no longer to be designed with 'A' or 'D' ends. In order to achieve reversibility with an automatic coupler, a number of the train wires had to be duplicated so that 64 studs were now required on the electrical connections of the coupler. Reversibility was considered to be desirable for stock working on the Central Line because of the existence of the Woodford-Hainault Loop.

If the Woodford-Hainault Loop had been operated as a through route instead of Hainault being used as a terminal station, the wrong way train problem would have been introduced as a normal condition on the Central Line. Even with this pattern of service with Hainault depot being situated adjacent to the terminal station, wrong way trains arose from the method of stabling the stock. To avoid the operation of wrong way trains in general service it was necessary for them to re-enter service in the same direction that they stabled at Hainault, but on occasions this could not be maintained and so all the Central Line 1962 Tube stock had to carry the 'D'-to-'D' coupling adaptors. The 1960 Tube stock was designed to avoid this problem entirely.

All the wheels on the motor bogies were the normal tube stock size — 31in diameter — when new. The car floor, unlike the previous tube stock designs, was flat, with no raised portion over the bogies to give clearance for the motors. The negative shoegear was supported from the bogie frame and not partly from the traction motor case. The bogies had rubber suspension for both the body bolster and the axle boxes, together with large shock absorbers called dampers. The bogies were arranged for double-block braking, that is two blocks per wheel almost diametrically opposed but each block being provided with its own brake cylinder.

The layout of doors and seating arrangement was similar to that provided in 1959 Tube stock driving motor cars but was slightly modified to allow a 'stand back' at the double door draught screen. In addition there was a complete redesign of the window arrangement. One each side of the car were provided six double-width windows, two for each of the three bays of seating between the sliding doors. Each door slid into pockets behind these

large windows. A double-glazing effect was brought about by the provision of interior hinged-frame casement lights the same size as the outside windows. The ventilation was provided above these casement lights by quadrant ventilators opening into a ducting, with the ventilator frames carrying the line route diagrams. This type of ventilator was designed to enable the cars to pass through the water washing machines without the ventilators having to be closed by staff beforehand.

The lighting was provided by 4ft 40W fluorescent tubes under-run at 32V,

mounted in two continuous lines of eight lamps along the monitor rail. Two of the fluorescent tubes were fed from the 50V dc battery through a transistor invertor to act as emergency lights should the motor alternator set shut down. These two tubes would remain alight as long as power was available in the battery.

The motor alternator set had an output of 6kW at 220V ac single-phase, 850 hertz; the fluorescent tubes were fed at 110V by means of a step-down transformer. The dc at 50V required for control purposes and for battery charg-

*Left:*
**The 1960 Tube stock driving position before modification for ATO.** *LRT 1900/4*

*Above:*
**A 1960 tube stock bogie.** *LRT*

ing was obtained from a separate winding on the transformer feeding a germanium full-wave rectifier.

The voltage regulation of the supply from the alternator was maintained by transistorised static equipment with no moving parts, avoiding the heavy maintenance inherent in the moving carbon voltage regulator provided with the 1938 and 1959 Tube stock equipments.

The exterior finish, similar to that provided on the 1959 Tube stock, consisted of aluminum alloy sheets riveted to a steel frame. On this stock, however, interior painting was also reduced to a minimum by the use of melamine-faced plastic panelling, with grab poles provided either in aluminium with a satin finish or in stainless steel. The ceiling was of painted pegboard with a view to improving sound absorption.

The fleet of the 1960 Tube stock prototype trains went into passenger service on the Central Line as an eight-car train on 9 November 1960. The motor cars were numbered in the series 39xx and the converted trailers in the series 49xx.

Partly because it was found that the cost of conversion of the trailer cars to run with these motor cars was high; partly because it was not possible to

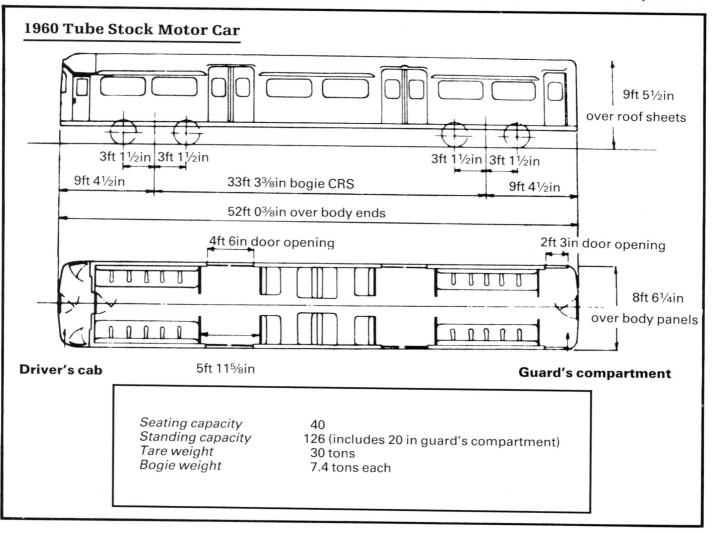

## 1960 Tube Stock Motor Car

9ft 5½in over roof sheets

3ft 1½in | 3ft 1½in     3ft 1½in | 3ft 1½in

9ft 4½in          33ft 3⅜in bogie CRS          9ft 4½in

52ft 0⅜in over body ends

4ft 6in door opening          2ft 3in door opening

8ft 6¼in over body panels

**Driver's cab**          5ft 11⅝in          **Guard's compartment**

| | |
|---|---|
| Seating capacity | 40 |
| Standing capacity | 126 (includes 20 in guard's compartment) |
| Tare weight | 30 tons |
| Bogie weight | 7.4 tons each |

prove the design of the new motor cars quickly enough to meet the immediate needs of the Central Line; and partly because by this time the performance of the 1959 Tube stock was very satisfactory, the intention to re-equip this line in this manner was abandoned and the replacement stock subsequently ordered was based on the proved design of 1959 Tube stock.

The conversion work on the trailers at Acton Works included the fitting of fluorescent lighting inside the cars, provision of external door-indicator lights and the painting of the outside silver to match the unpainted driving motor cars. Twelve cars were originally converted from the Pre-1938 Tube stock fleet. Four of the cars were of 1927 vintage and therefore only had four air doors per side. Nevertheless, two of these latter cars were reconstructed to provide end single doors. The other eight cars were from the 1931 fleet built by Birmingham or Gloucester, and already had end single doors as-built.

Later four of these converted trailers were fitted with de-icing equipment, after these units were relegated to the Roding Valley shuttle service between Hainault and Woodford as four-car units. They were used for service trials of a number of developments, not the least of which was Automatic Train Operation.

By 1974 the Pre-1938 Tube stock

trailer cars were becoming a serious maintenance liability, justifying the earlier decision not to proceed with further conversions. Arrangements were then made to replace these cars with the 1938 Tube stock trailer cars then becoming available from the scrapping programme. The conversion proposals envisaged that the units would be reduced to three cars so that only six 1938 Tube stock trailers would be required, as this would meet the service requirements. The 1938 Tube stock trailer cars would be fitted with two compressors, the previous trailers having one each. Arising from other developments and because the conversion work became expensive, only three units were in fact completed. In 1980/81 the two remaining units, 3904-4904-4905-3905, and 3900-4900-4901-3901, were refurbished and repainted at Hainault depot. The trailer cars were in fact painted white instead of the silver (aluminium) previously used.

In 1963 equipment was tried out on the District Line for the automatic control of trains. As a result of this experiment it was decided to equip the Woodford-Hainault branch of the Central Line for a full scale trial of Automatic Train Operation in preparation for use on the Victoria Line.

Five of the six 1960 Tube stock four-car units were therefore converted at Acton Works for use on this section

under automatic control conditions. In order to make these cars available for this experiment, three additional eight-car trains of 1962 Tube stock were ordered for the main Central Line service.

The alterations chiefly affected the driver's cab, and the main physical body change was the sealing of the driver's cab, access being confined to the front door or from the passenger saloon. The tripcock resetting cord was altered so that it could be reset from the front of the cab without the operator having to get down on to the track. The 'black boxes' containing the sensing equipment for automatic control were fitted under the cross seats in the passenger saloon.

The door control equipment was transferred from the normal guard's gangway position at the trailing end of the motor cars into the driver's cab. The driver — now renamed 'train operator' — occupied the leading cab and was required to open and close the doors and press the starting buttons. From then onwards the train proceeded under the control of the automatic signalling installation until brought to a stop at the next station automatically. Re-starts after intermediate signalling stops when the line was clear was automatic, without the train operator being required to do anything, but re-starts from a station stop required

*Left:*
**The interior of the 1960 Tube stock showing the pegboard type material used on the ceiling.** *LRT*

*Above:*
**One of the Pre-1938 Tube stock after conversion to run with the 1960 Tube stock motor cars.** *LRT*

the pressing of the starting buttons. A cabside drop window interlocked with the starting circuit ensured that the train did not start up with the operator's head out of the window.

The control signals were picked up from the track by coils mounted on the leading end of the first motor bogie. Two completely independent sets of coils were provided, placed in such a position that they sensed both running rails. One set of coils picked up the most important signals, the safety coded track circuits which were continuously received. Any failure to pick up a safety code signal caused the trip valve on the train to operate and the brakes to be applied. The trip valve took the place of the tripcock on the conventional rolling stock, which normally came in contact with a train-stop on the track if a danger signal was passed. On the trial rolling stock, although a trip valve was installed, the tripcock was retained and mechanical interlocking was provided so that only one system could be cut out at a time. This arrangement enabled these trains to operate outside the Automatic Train Control area. In addition, on the Hainault-Woodford section, the train-stops and conventional signals were retained because the tracks were used by conventional trains to reach Hainault depot.

The other set of pick-up coils sensed the signal commands provided to initiate all the driving instructions, including stopping at signals and stations. These commands were intermittent, being provided on the track only where and when required. When the train was approaching a station under instructions to stop, the commands given were associated with the speed at which the train should be running and fed into an electronic counter contained in the 'black box' under the seat. This speed indication was compared with a frequency produced by a generator mounted on one of the traction motors. This comparison indicated whether the train was travelling faster or slower than the ideal, and the braking power was increased or reduced accordingly until the train came to rest within a margin of a very few feet.

The accuracy of the station stop could be increased by the addition of more commands in the series. Coasting and signal commands did not need spot accuracy but were picked up by the same coils.

In addition to the provision of the frequency generator working with an electronic governor to detect the actual train speed with accuracy, a mechanical governor was also provided. Because there was insufficient space on the motor cars, this mechanical governor was fitted to the trailer axle adjacent to the motor car and can be said to be the most important safety equipment on the train. The governor had several speed settings which had to be set accurately, and operated in conjunction with the trip valve, having an overriding control over the electronic governor which worked in conjunction with the frequency generator and in fact checked that it had responded to the information provided by these devices.

The 25mph governor contacts, for example, were in circuit with the relays on the train corresponding to limited speed codes on the track, and if 25mph was exceeded when these codes were being received the emergency brake was applied by the operation of the trip valve. The mechanical governor was a fail-safe device in most circumstances, but in order to avoid false operation through wheel slide, cast iron blocks were fitted to the wheels on the axle providing the drive for the mechanical governor. This reduced the brake on this axle and made sure that maximum adhesion was obtained.

It was considered that a public address system was desirable because only one man was to be in charge of the train, so the cars were fitted with four loudspeakers in each passenger saloon. A hand-microphone type of instrument was provided in the cab; in order that the operator's mouth was maintained at the correct distance for clear enunciation, this was a telephone-type instrument, although the earpiece was not required for direct communication with the car interiors.

The first train went into service on 5 April 1964 and subsequently a service of automatic trains has been maintained over the Hainault-

Woodford Line since. A maximum of four trains were required for passenger service. The operation enabled experiments in train control to be carried out in preparation for the Victoria Line and for the development of the 1967 Tube stock.

The first unit to be operated with ATO equipment was 3910-4902-4903-3911, and the special equipment required was placed in the motor cars between the driver's cab and the first pair of double doors, reducing the space available for passengers. This enabled observations and adjustments to be made during the equipment's experimental period without the service being interrupted or the train placed over an inspection pit.

Although there were a total of six four-car units of 1960 Tube stock available, only five were converted for ATO working in passenger service. The first test unit, 3910-4902-4903-2911, became an Engineers' Test Train and was subsequently transferred to the service stock fleet as a track recording unit. Subsequently, although a 1938 Tube stock trailer car (012331) was earmarked to replace the two Pre-1938 Tube stock cars (4902 and 4903) in this unit, the make-up of the train in this way was never completed because of problems on the 1960 Tube stock involving the asbestos sound-proofing material. The car was in fact renumbered TRC912 to conform to the train recording duty it was to perform, but

the 1960 Tube stock cars were scrapped and a decision was made to obtain a specially-built track recording train from British Railways workshops.

For operation on the Hainault Loop (as it was sometimes called), one of the trailer cars in each unit was fitted with de-icing equipment. This equipment was in fact placed on the five even-numbered trailers, that is 4900-4904-4906-4910. In 1975, during overhaul at Acton Works, the two trailer cars of unit 3908-4908-4909-3909 were withdrawn for scrapping and replaced by a 1938 Tube stock trailer car, 012392, which was then renumbered 4929 and fitted with de-icing equipment as well as two compressors.

Later, two more trains had 1938 Tube stock trailer cars inserted to make three-car formations, but the work was considerably delayed by the need to take special precautions in the renovation of the 1960 Tube stock motor cars arising from the original asbestos soundproofing material. The units when completed then operated in the formations: 3902-4929-3903, 3906-4927-3907 and 3908-4921-3909, but the last unit did not enter service until 22 March 1981.

Although 1938 Tube stock trailers were selected for the purpose, two units

(3900-4900-4901-3901 and 3904-4904-4905-3905) did not have the conversion work carried out. These older trailer cars received minor internal renovations which kept them operational for a short time. They were withdrawn in 1982 and scrapped, but the motor cars have been stored.

Before conversion, 3902-4910-4911-3903 was fitted with thyristor control and was used with this equipment for a time in late-1975, but subsequently this was removed and the unit, with 4910-4911 replaced by the 1938 Tube stock trailer, was then converted to operate as a Fully Automatic Controlled Train (FACT) for future developments as an engineering test train. This work was completed in May 1983 and the unit returned to normal duty.

These units have often been used for technical experiments including service trials: for example 3904-4904-4905-3905 was equipped with the new type of passenger emergency device which was a key resettable push button instead of a handle. A handle could be operated and replaced so that the location of the emergency operation in train could not be found. This new arrangement required the attendance of a train operator to reset the device. It was later applied to all new rolling stock.

*Below:*
**The interior of Pre-1938 Tube stock after conversion to run with 1960 Tube stock. The 600V type filament lighting has been replaced by fluorescent tubing.** *LRT*

# 19.  1967 Tube Stock

The rolling stock designed for use on the Victoria Line, the first completely new tube line to be constructed across London for over 60 years, was based on the successful experiment for Automatic Train Operation on the Woodford-Hainault branch of the Central Line. It used modified 1960 Tube stock but additionally incorporated a number of new features.

The trains for the Victoria Line were of eight-car length made up with two identical four-car units, each consisting of a M-T-T-M formation having Wedglock type automatic couplers at the outer ends, with semi-permanent couplers between the cars of the unit. The Wedglock couplers provided the mechanical, electrical and pneumatic connectors between units but, because it was not proposed to provide for service uncoupling, the associated disconnecting units were arranged for manual operation sequentially from adjacent cabs instead of simultaneously as provided previously.

The trains were built by Metropolitan-Cammell Ltd and were provided with a 'new look', including double-width side windows; pull-down internal ventilators with external slots (first introduced on the 1960 Tube stock) gave a double-glazing effect. The most striking feature of the new car body design was the wrap-round front windows of the driving cab, which provided a wide-angle vision for the train operator. Another change in window design was in the air-operated doors, because the glass had been taken up into the curved part of the door to allow passengers in the doorways to look out without stooping.

The interior seating arrangement provided in the motor cars followed the 1960 Tube stock with cross-seats in the centre bay and with a 'stand back'

*Below:*
**The Victoria Line 1967 Tube stock. The calling-on light is at the top right-hand of the car front. A pick-up coil can just be seen in front of the truck.** *LRT H16377*

arranged for standing passengers in the double doorways. Stand backs were also provided in the trailer cars where the seating was entirely longitudinal. The seats themselves were all combined, seat and back upholstered with moquette, with armrests of a new two-level style made of glass fibre.

The driver's cab had been designed to facilitate one-man operation of the train, and in addition to the automatic driving controls contained a single master controller for both power and braking for manual drive when necessary. The cab also contained door control boxes, one for each side of the

train. The single traction/brake controller was provided at the conventional left-hand side of the cab and was designed to incorporate all the features required for automatic operation. The change from automatic to manual could be arranged easily without the train operator leaving his seat. In the event

that manual control was required, without safety codes being received, the appropriate flag switch had to be raised, which then allowed speeds up to 10mph without an emergency brake application. Such operation was normally only required within the depot.

# 1967 Tube Stock

## Motor Car 1967 Stock

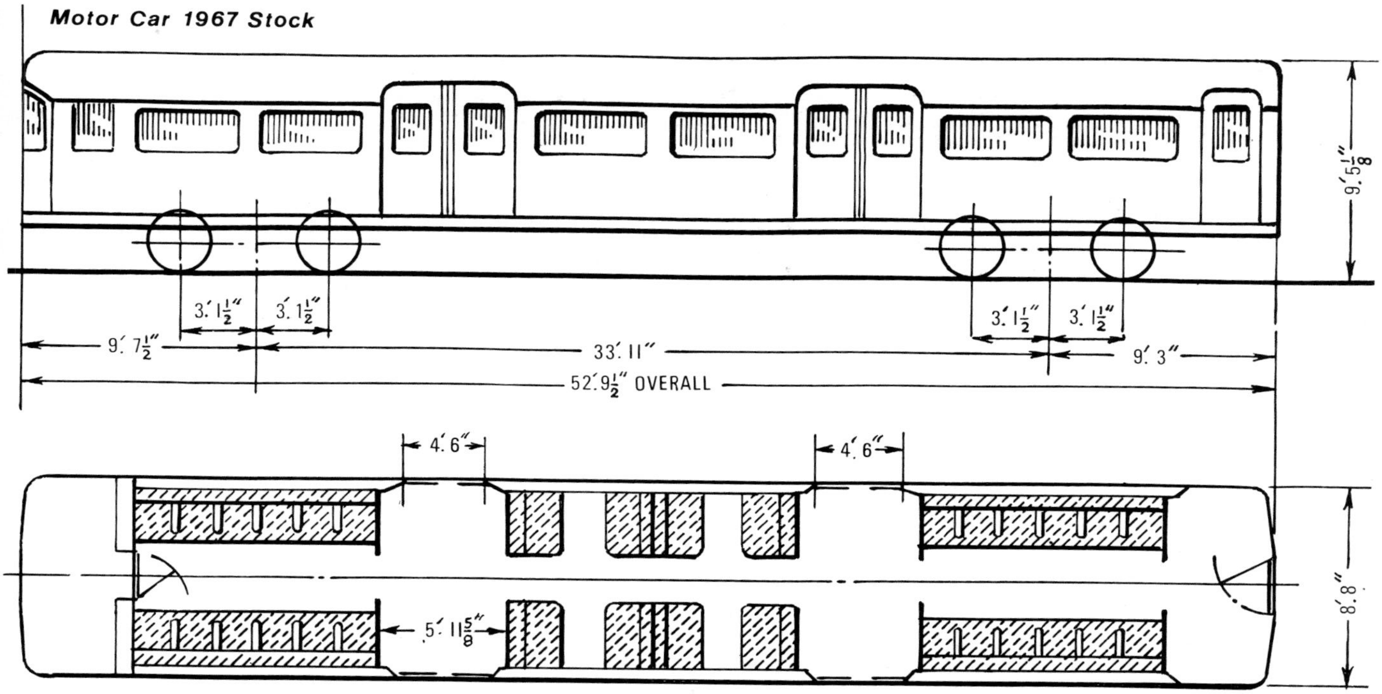

9' 5⅛"

3' 1½"  3' 1½"

9' 7½"

33' 11"

3' 1½"  3' 1½"

9' 3"

52' 9½" OVERALL

4' 6"          4' 6"

5' 11⅝"

8' 8"

## Trailer Car 1967 Stock

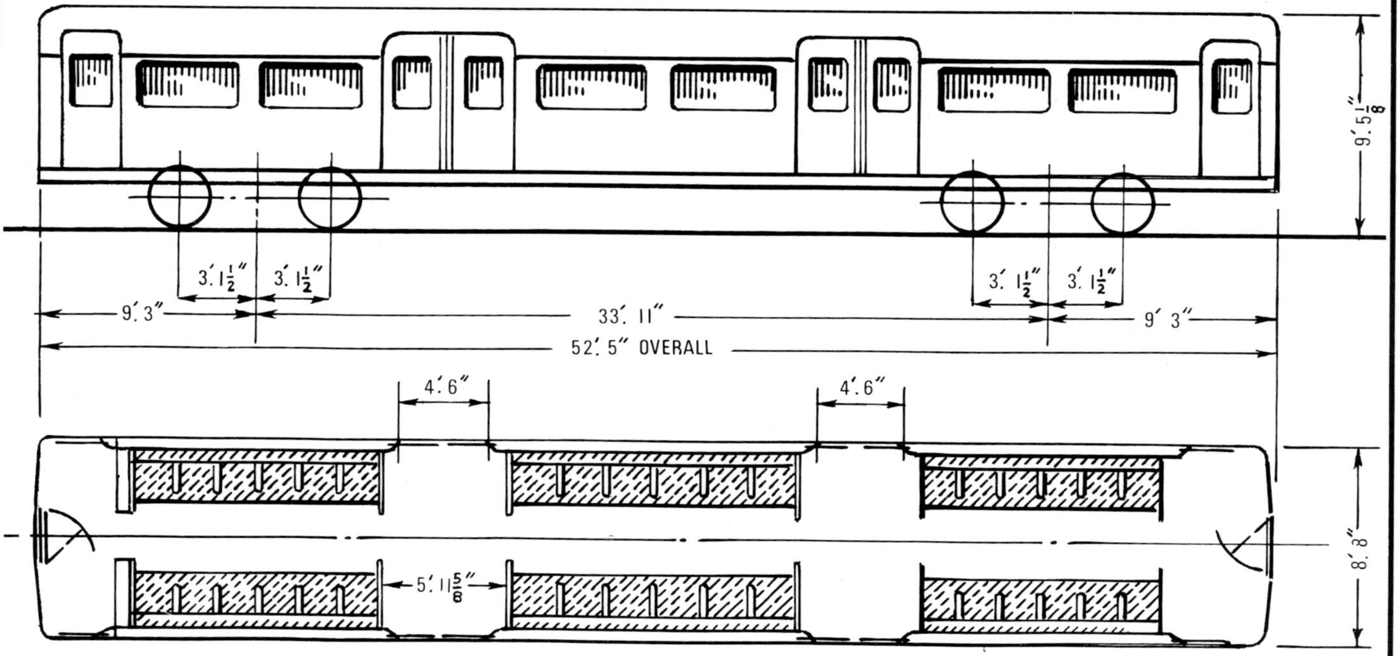

9' 5⅛"

3' 1½"  3' 1½"

9' 3"

33' 11"

3' 1½"  3' 1½"

9' 3"

52' 5" OVERALL

4' 6"          4' 6"

5' 11⅝"

8' 8"

Another new emergency control feature incorporated for the first time in tube stock was the provision of a fault isolating switch, which enabled the train operator in the event of control trouble to isolate from his leading cab either of the two four-car units which made up the train, yet operate the control from the leading cab controller.

This was achieved without increasing the number of control wires carried across the Wedglock coupler but required the provision of additional unit wires carried across the semi-permanent couplings.

For the first time the entire control equipment was fitted with cam-operated micro-switches. These were fitted to the traction brake controller disconnecting unit, fault-isolating switches and door and other control switches, some hundred being required on each train. This type of equipment reduced considerably the examination of electrical contacts as a maintenance procedure. The traction control gear, although still of the well-tried PCM type, incorporated switching for rheostatic braking for the first time on tube stock. With this, the traction motors were used as generators, loading the power developed in stopping the train on to rheostats. The arrangement for the braking ensured that priority was given to the rheostatic braking, which developed up to its maximum capability followed by the application of the friction brake on the trailer cars. To this could be added (if and when necessary) the air-applied friction brakes on the motor cars. If the rheostatic braking should fail or when the rheostatic brake faded below 10mph, the friction brake was applied.

The air friction brake was electro-pneumatic in operation with plug-in type valves under the control of mercury retarders so that either a maximum, normal or minimum brake was made under automatic control. The rheostatic brake application was not affected, remaining unaltered to give minimum braking, the air brakes providing the controllable additional braking force as required. By this means the rheostatic braking control was kept as simple as possible.

The motor cars were each provided with four Crompton Parkinson Type LT115 traction motors, connected two in permanent series. The motors were axle-hung with spur gearing and a ratio of 16:65, so that a higher armature speed was required than on previous tube stock. This enabled the motors to be smaller, allowing a flat floor to be arranged.

As 1967 Tube stock had to be controlled by one man, a very effective hand brake was required, and this was achieved by the provision of a hydraulic applied brake which, after application, was locked on until released by hydraulic pressure. A complete brake application was sufficient to hold a loaded train on the worst gradient, and this could be achieved without too much physical effort by the train operator.

The fluorescent car lighting tubes were disposed further round the ceilings than previously and were fed with a 115V, 850 hertz ac supply, but two of the tubes were fed with dc through a static invertor from the battery and these therefore remained alight if the motor alternator shut down while the lights were switched on.

Car heating was supplied in a new manner by the use of 'mat' type heaters designed by the English Electric Co, spread over the seat risers. Another innovation on this stock was the provision of a number of illuminated interior roof advertisements.

The motor cars carried two designs of motor alternator sets. Those provided by AEI generated 850 hertz ac supply at 230V, which was stepped down by transformer to 115V for the supply to the fluorescent lighting and to 58V to supply the rectifier feeding

*Far left:*
**The right-hand side bulkhead panel, with door controller and handbrake wheel, of the 1967 Tube stock.** *LRT 68/979*

*Above:*
**The offside console of 1967 Tube stock.** *LRT 68/983*

the 50V battery. The English Electric MAR units consisted of an alternator providing 60V, 850 hertz, the lighting supply at 115V being obtained by a step-up transformer. The alternator supply in this case was connected directly to a rectifier which fed the 50V battery.

The compressors (Reavell type) were carried on the trailer cars, which also carried the mechanical governors required for ATO. This was a centrifugal device driven by a simple spur gear mounted on a trailer axle. The contacts

on the mechanical governor provided some of the safety controls required for ATO.

The bogies provided on the 1967 Tube stock followed the general design of the 1960 Tube stock but included the use of sandwich-type side bearers for the first time. Although each brake block had an individual brake cylinder, only one block pressed on each wheel since a great deal of the braking was achieved rheostatically. All the bogies were provided with Timken tapered roller bearings.

**1972 Tube stock Mk II with red-painted doors. Note the London Transport roundel instead of the 'Underground' fleet name and the provision of the calling-on light at top right-hand of the cab.** *LRT 14128-1*

Additional communication systems were provided on the 1967 Tube stock because only one train operator was carried. The system included:

● A carrier wave system which provided communication between the traffic controller and the train operator. The carrier wave system utilised the traction current rails for the transmission of the communication. One advantage was that the system could be used while the trains were on the move, but had the disadvantage that it could not be operated if the current had been discharged, and a short-circuiting bar has been placed on the track connecting the two current rails together on occasion when a reliable communication system would be desirable.

● A public address system which enabled the train operator to speak to the passengers from any driving cab.

● A cab-to-cab telephone, enabling the train operator or other staff to speak between the front and the rear of the train.

● Calling-on lights and inter-train radio, links which enabled the train operator of a defective train at the leading end to communicate with the train behind without leaving his cab. The calling-on light was used to notify the train behind that it was expected that it would approach and couple up. The assisting train radio was considered to be a back-up only, because telephone could be used once the trains were coupled cab-to-cab.

The original order for 1967 Tube stock was for 61 four-car interchangeable units with the formation M-T-T-M, the 'A' end (north) cars being numbered 3001-3061 and the 'D' end (south) cars numbered 3101-3161, with the adjacent cars numbered between 4001 and 4161. The numbers utilised were those used in earlier years for Pre-1938 Tube stock motor cars and District Line motor cars which had now been scrapped. Upon the extension to Brixton a further 18 units were required. These units were identical to those delivered earlier and continued the numbering scheme.

Following delivery from Metropolitan-Cammell at Birmingham to Ruislip depot (where the cars were prepared for service) and before any part of the new Victoria Line was available, units were transferred to Hainault depot for ATO trials in four-car formation over the Hainault-Woodford Line. Following this important checking, the units were then brought to Northumberland Park by battery locomotives over Eastern Region tracks by means of the connection with the Central Line at Leytonstone (which has now been removed). After the first stage of the Victoria Line was opened in September 1968, the

106

*Above:*
**The driver's console of 1967 Tube stock.** *LRT 68/984*

junction between the Piccadilly Line and the Victoria Line at Finsbury Park became available for rolling stock transfers.

From time to time a four-car unit of 1967 Tube stock has worked in passenger service on the Hainault-Woodford service to enable the shuttle units to be modified and overhauled. These units were returned to the Victoria Line when necessary.

With the upsurge in traffic on the Underground system following the simplification of the fare structure, it became desirable to improve the service on the Victoria Line as well as the other tube lines. Because of the ATO special provisions, the 1967 Tube stock was somewhat unique, and other types of stock could not operate on the line. To overcome this factor without buying new trains specially for the Victoria Line, it was decided that by making

some of the four-car units into a kind of uncoupling unit by utilising some 1972 Tube stock Mk I motor cars in middle positions, where ATO equipment was not required an expansion of the fleet could be arranged. The introduction with a minimum of modification of 1972 Tube stock Mk I motor cars — whose car bodies, physical appearance, traction and auxiliary equipment was compatible — released some 1967 Tube stock motor cars with ATO equipment to work on leading ends only. Two trains of 1972 Tube stock Mk I would then provide an additional 1½ trains of virtually 1967 Tube stock, leaving two uncoupling non-driving motor cars unused. The final stock adjustments would depend on the number of additional trains eventually required on the Victoria Line and the availability of other stocks to fill the gap created in the Northern Line fleet.

# 20. 1972 Tube Stock

By 1970 it was necessary to consider the future of the 1938 Tube stock which at that time comprised a fleet of 1,278 cars, most of which dated from about the year of the title. Past experience of the life of rolling stock with painted steel bodies and equipped with rubber-sheathed electrical wiring indicated that the normal economic life was not more than 35 years. An extension of life was possible by a major reconstruction including major rewiring, but without the expenditure of very large sums of money even these improvements would not overcome obsolescence.

In 1970 the 1938 Tube stock provided the entire fleet of the Bakerloo and Northern Lines and, in addition, a few trains on the Piccadilly Line. The Northern Line required a fleet of 840 cars, most of which were made up into seven-car trains composed of four- and three-car units, but in addition required a small number of six-car formations composed of two three-car units for the Highbury Branch (the newly adopted name of the Northern City Line).

Although the 1938 Tube stock had served the Northern Line for over 30 years, this had not been achieved without some operating difficulties, not the least of which was the limitation in flexibility arising out of the handing of the units and the operation of the Kennington Loop. Handing as a principle is satisfactory for lines which operate as shuttles without operations round loops or triangles which cause trains to be turned. A loop offers operating advantages, but when the stock is handed, coupling disadvantages arise. The Northern Line has suffered continually from the disadvantage of handed rolling stock since the introduction of the first loop at Charing Cross in 1914, a problem continued because the Kennington Loop is now an integral part of the operation of the line. While some of the disadvantage can be offset by the provision of additional spare train units and turntables, there are always times when these provisions are insufficient.

In considering the provision of replacement rolling stock, therefore, some thought was given to eliminating this problem on the Northern Line. The first design proposed an eight-car train composed of two four-car articulated units with the same train length as a seven-car train. Each four-car unit was to be identical, interchangeable in position on the eight-car formation, and have reversible coupling facilities. The overall length of the train was of course limited by the existing platform lengths, some of which were already tight for seven-car 1938 Tube stock.

The proposal for articulation was the carrying of two car body ends on a common bogie, and this, with slightly smaller body lengths, would enable an eight-car train to approximate to the same length as a conventional seven-car train. Preliminary designs and feasibility studies were made and an articulated bogie was constructed, but before the work could be brought to a successful conclusion and authority obtained for the purchase of rolling

---

*Below:*
**A seven-car train of 1972 Tube stock Mk I with Wedglock type coupler for mechanical coupling only.** *LRT 3831/2*

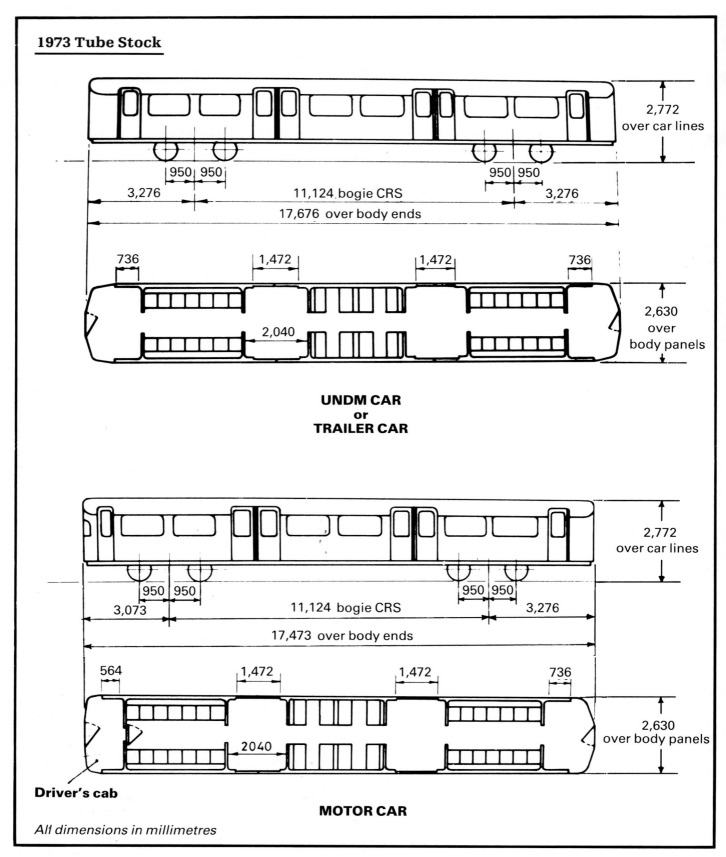

**UNDM CAR
or
TRAILER CAR**

**Driver's cab**

**MOTOR CAR**

*All dimensions in millimetres*

stock based on this design for operation on the Northern Line, the go-ahead was given for the construction of the Heathrow extension of the Piccadilly Line.

The decision to provide the extension into Heathrow required a reappraisal of the rolling stock arrangements, out of which the eight-car articulated concept

for the Northern Line became a casualty. This assessment of the rolling stock requirements resulted in a need for additional trains on the Piccadilly Line. A decision was then made to re-equip the Piccadilly Line completely, thus encompassing the needs of the Heathrow extension, releasing the 1959 Tube stock fleet for transfer to the

Northern Line to replace the 1938 Tube stock.

Unfortunately the fleet of the 1959 Tube stock was insufficient to meet the total needs of that line, necessitating the provision of some additional trains to provide the balance. To reduce the financial burden of purchasing a large block of new rolling stock, a study of the condition of the 1938 Tube stock was undertaken to see whether the life of any vehicle could be extended for at least 10 years.

Following this appraisal, proposals were made to recondition some 88 trains of 1938 Tube stock — 52 for the Bakerloo Line, six for the Highbury branch of the Northern Line and 30 to make up the balance of trains required for the Northern Line, to make up the total fleet after the transfer of the 1959 Tube stock following the provision of rolling stock of an entirely new design for the Piccadilly Line.

Provision of rolling stock of a new design inevitably takes a considerable time to develop and build. However, political pressure arose to improve conditions on the Northern Line sooner rather than later, and it was therefore decided to purchase as quickly as possible 30 new trains of an existing basic design for operation on the Northern Line. In consequence, the reconstruction of 1938 Tube stock was reduced to 58 trains, the number required for the Bakerloo Line and the Highbury branch.

Having recently built rolling stock for the Victoria Line, an order was placed in 1971 with Metro-Cammell for 30 trains of seven-car formation of a similar basic design to the 1967 Tube stock. These trains were then designated 1972 Tube stock because there were several differences incorporated. They were in fact not interchangeable with the earlier stock which they resembled.

The 1967 Tube stock provided for the Victoria Line was formed into eight-car trains made up of two identical units. The 1972 Tube stock trains, however, were required in seven-car formations to operate on the Northern Line so that it was necessary to form them by providing four- and three-car units. In addition, provision had to be made for two-man operation as against the one-man operation of the Victoria Line.

The four-car units consisted of two driving motor cars with two trailers placed between them — similar in fact to the four-car units provided for the Victoria Line — but the motor cars were provided with a guard's control console in the traditional position at the trailing end of the passenger compartment. Unlike the four-car units of 1967 Tube stock which were handed because the Victoria Line was a straight shuttle-type service, the 1972 Tube stock four-car units were reversible, so that problems arising from traversing the Kennington Loop would not produce 'wrong way' trains.

To achieve this reversibility the three-car unit was made up of one driving motor (also carrying guard's consoles in the traditional position at the trailing end of the passenger compartment), a trailer car, and an uncoupling non-driving motor car. This latter car was a motor car without a

traditional driving position, having the passenger compartment almost identical to the trailer car. However, this car was provided not only with a shunting control cabinet enclosed in the end bulkhead but an autocoupler as well. The autocouplers, which were fitted to the motor cars of the four-car unit and the uncoupling non-driving motor cars of the three-car unit, were so designed that coupling could be achieved at either end of a four-car unit. In this way the three-car unit could couple to either end of a four-car unit to make a seven-car train, which overcame the handing problem.

The shunting control cabinet (not a new feature, having been first introduced with the 1949 Tube stock which augmented the 1938 Tube stock fleet) enabled the three-car unit to be shunted in yards and depots at slow speed with maximum safety. The driving motor car of the three-car units was always at the outer end of a seven-car train, and therefore, unlike the non-driving motor car which had an automatic coupler, was provided with a mechanical coupler for use in an emergency only, when assisting a disabled train.

The traction control, including rheostatic braking, incorporated the same basic design as fitted to the 1967 Tube stock: each traction control unit on each motor car controlled four 300V traction motors. Two motors, operated permanently in series, were mounted on each bogie, but all four motors operated together in a series-parallel connection.

A feature of the control was the combined traction brake controller, first introduced in the 1967 Tube stock, but incorporating a deadman's safety device which had to be controlled while the handle was in the driving position. This controller was different from that provided on 1967 Tube stock, which was designed for ATO with manual driving under controlled speeds only. Tripcocks were of course fitted to the driving motor car leading bogies. The bogies were otherwise similar to those provided for 1967 Tube stock, having 31in (787mm) diameter wheels and a wheelbase of 6ft 3in (1.905m).

The uncoupling non-driving motor car had a length over body ends of 52ft 5in (15.98m), the same dimensions as the trailer cars. The driving motor cars were 4½in (114mm) longer over body ends and included a wrap-round window in front of the driver's cab.

The interior arrangements were similar in most details to that of the 1967 Tube stock including fluorescent lighting, illuminated adverts and set-back door screens to accommodate a limited number of standing passengers without obstructing the doorways. The seating arrangements on the trailer cars were all longitudinal, giving a seating capacity of 36 but providing more standing space. Motor cars continued

to be fitted with cross-seats in the middle bays to give some additional space required for housing equipment. The provision of these cross-seats raised the seating of the car to 40. The longitudinal seats in all the cars had the two level-type armrests which were devised to enable adjacent passengers to share the same armrest without difficulty.

When it was decided to buy some additional trains of this same basic design, the first batch of 30 trains were given the designation Mk 1. The first train of this type began working on the Northern Line on 26 June 1972.

The decision to obtain a completely new design of train, incorporating many new features for operation on the Piccadilly Line arising out of the authorisation of the extension to Heathrow Airport, inevitably created a gap in the continuous construction programme of rolling stock, so it was decided to purchase a further 33 trains of 1972 Tube stock to fill the gap. It was possible to arrange to buy new trains in advance of the final replacement of the remaining 1938 Tube stock in addition to the purchase of the Piccadilly Line replacement stock. The reconstruction programme for 1938 Tube stock had been reduced to 58 trains after the decision to purchase 1972 Tube stock trains. The position had then become complicated by the decision to construct the first part of the Fleet Line, for which some additional rolling stock would be required.

It was then decided to reduce the number of reconstructed 1938 Tube stock trains from 58 to 34 since 18 trains would no longer be required for the Stanmore service which would be provided by the Fleet Line operation. Also a further six trains would not be required for the Highbury branch of the Northern Line because it had been decided to incorporate this line within the recently-authorised Great Northern electrification scheme of British Railways.

It was fortunate that the number of trains required for Stage I of the Fleet Line initially, was almost identical to that required for the operation of the Bakerloo Line service that remained after the transfer of the Stanmore branch. It therefore became possible to order a fleet of trains for the initial Fleet Line operation which would be subsequently used to replace the reconstructed fleet of 1938 Tube stock for short-term operation on the Bakerloo Line. Thus more modern stock could be provided later on the Fleet Line. It had been originally intended to provide ATO with one-man operation, but it was difficult to provide this arrangement immediately, because after six years' experience of the equipment installed on the Victoria Line it was considered unsatisfactory to repeat the equipment without incorporating fundamental alterations to overcome its

*Above:*
**The interior of a 1972 Tube stock trailer car showing longitudinal seats in the middle bay.** *LRT*

limitations and to take advantage of developing technology. The acquisition of more 1972 Tube stock trains at this stage enabled a delay of some years to be achieved for further development.

The provision of these additional 33 trains of 1972 Tube stock (designated Mk II), enabled not only the reconstruction of 1938 Tube stock to be confined to those required for the Bakerloo Line but enabled other 1938 Tube stock to be scrapped earlier in the programme by running this new stock on the Northern Line until the Fleet Line was opened.

Provision had been made in the Mk II design for conversion to ATO to be undertaken at the end of the time spent on the Northern Line. The ATO system proposed for the Fleet Line had incorporated a number of improvements to that used on the Victoria Line to give more accurate stopping, additional controlled speeds, and the use of coded track circuits compatible with the use in future of 'chopper' type control systems. However, due to the lack of resources and need for additional development time, it had been decided that the Mk II stock would then take

over the operations on the Bakerloo Line without any modification. New rolling stock could then have been designed for the Fleet Line. All that had then been rendered redundant by this change of mind was the built-in conversion arrangements to enable the 1972 Mk II stock to be converted to OMO/ATO. The installation to enable this to be achieved in any case had been minimal at the time of its construction.

The traction/brake controller of the Mk II trains was similar to that provided on the Mk I, with a deadman's feature operative in all positions except 'shut down' or 'hold'. The 'hold' position applied the initial rheostatic brake and was the position to which the controller was placed finally at station stops. The selector switch which unlocked the traction/brake controller was different, being provided with a position for 'auto' working which only became operative when and if the trains were modified and equipped for

ATO working. This position was made available on the selector key by providing only one 'Forward' selection. On the Mk I trains two positions were provided, 'forward 1' and 'forward 2', giving a low and high accelerating rate. These two rates were still provided on the Mk II trains but were selected by means of a separate switch which was located in the cab within easy reach of the operator.

In addition on the Mk II stock, two whistle buttons were provided, the additional one being located on the offside pillar of the cab for use under ATO conditions when the operator would not necessarily be at the driving console.

Many additional switches which would normally have been arranged for control by the guard had to be provided in the cab. These switches duplicated those provided on the guard's gangway position (which were still provided on the Mk II stock), but as long as two men

*Above:*
**An interior view of 1972 Tube stock looking towards the guard's door control panels on the end bulkheads.** *LRT 3831/7*

were employed — that is a driver and a guard — the switches in the cab were disconnected.

As far as passengers were concerned, the most important of the duplicated switching arrangements were the door controls, which made it possible for control to be exercised from the driver's cab instead of the guard's gangway at the trailing end of the motor car. These facilities were only provided in those motor cars which would be at the outer ends of the trains under ATO conditions. Loop working was not as yet envisaged as a procedure, with ATO/OMO operation for tube stock at that time being possible only on the Northern Line.

Another new feature on the Mk II stock was a motorised destination blind which could incorporate a positive identification feature. This equipment was a development beyond the Indentra provided on the Victoria Line which enabled not only the train

destination but its number and operating crew number to be transmitted to a central control computer. Such an arrangement would enable train controllers and station managers to locate trains and crews after a service dislocation and to assist timetable adjustments. This consisted of a rectangular box mounted on the offside console, next to the emergency brake handle, on which there were three rows of figures with corresponding thumbnail wheels. Each row of figures denoted the train number, destination and crew number respectively. When the appropriate destination code was set the motorised blind revolved to display the correct destination to the public in the box above the centre cab door. When the train number sequence was operated after the destination light was switched on, the numbers were displayed by illuminated figures designed to be visual at the front of the train. Until this equipment could be brought into

use a conventional train number display bracket was provided similar to that installed on Mk I stock. Difficulties with the motorised blind led to the eventual removal of this equipment. The original design of electronic train number indicator also gave rise to difficulties, especially in strong sunlight conditions, and this arrangement was also removed. Thus the Mk II trains became similar to the Mk I trains in this respect too.

Twelve trailer cars of Mk II stock were fitted with de-icing equipment, including sprays and tanks to hold the fluid. In addition, sleet brushes were fitted to the leading bogies of all the driving motor cars. These sleet brushes were raised and lowered by means of pneumatic cylinders electrically controlled from the cab. A visual cab display was also fitted to indicate the position of the de-icing equipment and the sleet brushes. All driving cabs had de-icing equipment control, even though they were not associated directly with the trailer cars carrying the equipment.

After delivery, these trains went into service on the Northern Line, the first train entering passenger service on 19 November 1973. Although supposedly interchangeable in operation, it was found that the two types of stock were incapable of coupling in all respects. Modifications to the electrical circuitry was therefore arranged to enable the Mk I and Mk II units to operate together in passenger service, but in the event this was rarely done. There was a difference in appearance between the types in that the sliding doors of the Mk II cars were painted red and generally they remained in separate train sets.

For a considerable time beginning in 1975 the Northern Line had to cope with four rolling stock types — namely the 1938 Tube stock, the 1959 Tube stock and the two marks of 1972 Tube stock. With the 1938 and 1959 Tube stocks being handed, the difficulty of 'wrong way' trains was also involved. This problem had of course been designed out of the 1972 formations.

In preparation for the opening of the Fleet Line in 1977, steps were taken in 1976 to transfer the Mk II trains one at a time to the Bakerloo Line, so that by the time the Fleet Line (now renamed the Jubilee Line) was due to open, all 33 trains were in position with the crews trained. In this way there was no difficulty in segregating the two services on the line — previously operated as a 'Y' — to two separate lines in parallel with 1972 Mk II trains on the Jubilee Line and the 1938 Tube stock on the Bakerloo Line. The first 1972 Mk II Tube stock train entered service on the Bakerloo Line on 4 April 1977.

One of the problems which arose with the 1972 Tube stock operating on the Bakerloo Line was the difficulty of crew reliefs at busy periods at such locations as Baker Street, because access to the cab was through the passenger compartment as there were no side cab doors provided. Access to the cab by way of the front cab door over the centre buffer was improved by the provision of step plates and additional grab-rails. In addition to this modification, units transferred to the Bakerloo Line were fitted with Storno-type radio, a two-way communication system.

The Jubilee Line was opened officially on 30 April 1979 and the two services were then segregated. Subsequently, when the 1983 Tube stock came on the scene, it was introduced to the Jubilee Line and some Mk II trains were returned to the Northern Line. The first such train re-entered service on 8 April 1983 after an absence of four years from the line.

Consideration is now being given to the conversion of the 1972 Mk II Tube stock trains to OPO. These trains were originally designed with single manning in mind, thus the modification required will be minimal. Additional communicating systems have to be installed to enable two-way speech to be arranged between the train operators and control centres, and to ensure that the train operator can call for the assistance of the following train in an emergency. The door controls are required to be located in the driving cabs and those already provided on the traditional guard's gangway rendered inoperative. Some provision for this had been built into the cars originally. A straight swop of 1959 Tube stock and 1972 Mk II Tube stock between the Northern and Bakerloo will enable this to be arranged with a minimum of disturbance. The 1972 Mk I Tube stock will remain on the Northern Line for the time being, except for the four cars which have been converted to enlarge the fleet of 1967 Tube stock on the Victoria Line to enable the service to be improved.

*Below:*
**A six-car train of 1973 Tube stock.** *LRT 3006/4/6*

# 21. 1973 Tube Stock

Following authority for the construction of the extension of the Piccadilly Line from Hounslow West right into Heathrow Airport, consideration had to be given to the provision of the rolling stock which would not only provide for the additional mileage arising but cover the additional traffic which was forecast. Controversy then arose concerning the type of train to be provided for service to an airport, as it was the opinion of several bodies interested in the project that luggage would be a major problem. It was therefore decided to provide entirely new rolling stock for the Piccadilly Line and include some provision for luggage. The 1959 Tube stock then operating on the Piccadilly Line was relatively new and did not require replacement, so the purchase of new stock entailed a considerable reshuffle of rolling stock between lines.

The design of a new type of train began in 1970 and was based on a six-car formation roughly equivalent in capacity to that of the seven-car trains then operating on tube lines. Authority was then given for sufficient trains of this new type to be obtained to provide the whole of the Piccadilly Line rolling stock requirement, including additional trains to cover the Heathrow extension. The 1959 Tube stock displaced was then to be used to enable a start to be made in replacing the 1938 Tube stock considered to be at the end of its economic life.

The six-car formation was chosen for several reasons, the main one being

that it reduced the number of bodies and bogies to be built for each train, thereby reducing the total cost. In addition it would enable a symmetrical train to be produced, helping maintenance and service reliability. The individual cars were about 6ft longer than the conventional type car, but the total length of the six-car train was about 17ft shorter than a seven-car 1959 Tube stock train. This was considered to be an advantage as some of the platforms were still tight for seven-car formations of older stock. Removing the guard from the conventional position at the gangway end of the motor cars to improve passenger accommodation

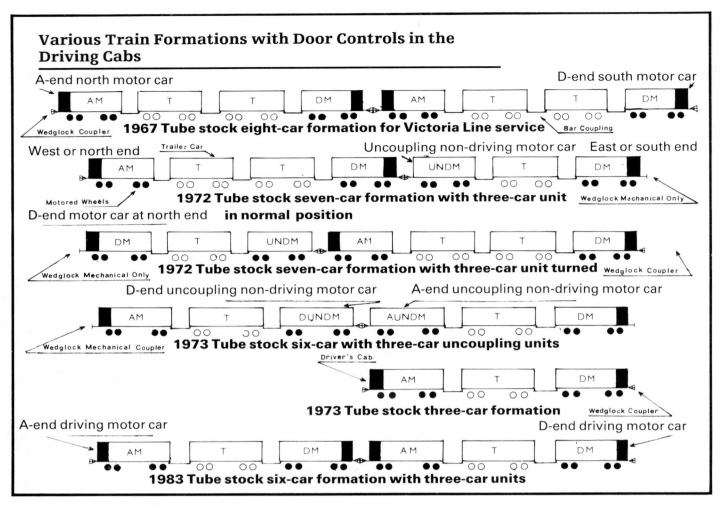

## Various Train Formations with Door Controls in the Driving Cabs

**1967 Tube stock eight-car formation for Victoria Line service**

A-end north motor car — D-end south motor car
Wedglock Coupler — Bar Coupling

**1972 Tube stock seven-car formation with three-car unit in normal position**

West or north end — Trailer Car — Uncoupling non-driving motor car — East or south end
Motored Wheels — Wedglock Mechanical Only

**1972 Tube stock seven-car formation with three-car unit turned**

D-end motor car at north end
Wedglock Mechanical Only — Wedglock Coupler

**1973 Tube stock six-car with three-car uncoupling units**

D-end uncoupling non-driving motor car — A-end uncoupling non-driving motor car
Wedglock Mechanical Coupler

**1973 Tube stock three-car formation**

Driver's Cab — Wedglock Coupler

**1983 Tube stock six-car formation with three-car units**

A-end driving motor car — D-end driving motor car

required the guard to be at the extreme end of the train.

The capacity of the six-car train was virtually the same as the conventional seven-car train, but the increased length of each car almost confined the rolling stock to the Piccadilly Line alone so that future interchange to other lines would be a doubtful proposition. The extra car length enabled specific space to be arranged for the accommodation of luggage, which at the same time could be utilised as improved standing accommodation on other parts of the Piccadilly Line service.

An order was placed with Metro-Cammell Ltd of Birmingham in 1970 for a total of 87 trains of six-car length, together with one three-car unit to enable the Aldwych shuttle service to be operated by the same stock. The trains were made up with two three-car units, and there were three kinds of such units. Most of the trains were made up of units of the motor-trailer-uncoupling non-driving motor formations coupled together to make a six-car train, with a driving motor only at the outer ends. As the cars were handed these units were 'A' ends and 'D' ends, with uncoupling non-driving motor cars having automatic couplers to couple together, while the driving motors were fitted with mechanical couplers only.

There were 77 of each type of these units. In addition there were 21 three-car units with driving motor cars (fitted with automatic couplers) at both ends. These units could be used to operate as single trains on the Aldwych shuttle but were required to substitute for either an 'A' end or 'D' end unit to make up a six-car train. The first three-car unit of 1973 Tube stock to operate on the Aldwych service began working on 18 October 1979, although the first double-ended unit had been delivered on 23 December 1976.

Following the pattern established with the 1956 Tube stock, the construction consisted of a welded-steel underframe with an unpainted aluminium car body fitted to it. Tube cars, because of their low height with restricted width, are built so that the underframe contains all the strength. Aluminium solebars have to be designed very large to provide the necessary strength, and exposed aluminium would require protection from electric arcing where there was close proximity to the third-rail collector shoes. For these reasons aluminium was not used for the strength members.

The maximum length of each car was dictated by the minimum track curvature on the Piccadilly Line, together with the limits imposed by the restricted loading gauge. Where the track curves at station platforms, gaps

between the car body at the door openings and the platforms can only be bridged by extending the doorway treadover plates, but these plates must not extend beyond the structure gauge. Platform curves are not particularly severe on the Piccadilly Line, so it was possible to produce a car of 58ft 6in (17.8m) in length without creating other problems. The maximum length which would be tolerated on the Central, Northern and Bakerloo Lines would be limited to 16m (52ft 6in), the limit for tube line rolling stock previously. The provision of cars of the longer length however, makes the transfer of rolling stock between lines less likely in future rolling stock programmes, each line becoming virtually a separate railway.

The length of a seven-car 1959 Tube stock train as operated on the Piccadilly Line was 113m (367ft), but the length of the six-car trains of 1973 Tube stock was shorter at 107m (350ft). The driver and guard on a two-man train can normally compensate for misjudgment in positioning the train at platforms by cutting out the end passenger doors by means of the cut-out switches provided. However, when one-person operation is arranged, such adjustments become more difficult so that it is desirable that all variations in stopping are contained within the total platform length.

With the possibility of OPO being

required at some time in the future, the door controls were provided in the driver's cab. Until converted to OPO, the doors were operated from the rear cab where the guard was positioned. For the first time on tube stock the driving cabs were provided with sliding doors with pneumatic seals, reducing the problem of draughts.

The passenger doors were controlled from panels on each side of the rear cab bulkhead. A feature introduced on this stock was the provision of a selective close button enabling all doors to be closed except two door leaves on each car and three door leaves on driving motor cars. In addition a door cut-out switch provided in the cab enabled the three leaves nearest the cab on driving motor cars to remain closed if the train overran or stopped short.

The doors themselves are now operated by a small light type of air engine unit which controls two door leaves at adjacent doorways by means of mechanical rodding. The single door leaf nearest the driver's cab on the driving motor cars was provided with a separate engine controlling only that leaf. The door leaves themselves are now top-hung, a system introduced on the 1972 Mk II stock is a break from the traditional method of providing curved-type tube air doors. All previous air door tube stock was provided with doors running on bottom tracks.

The air-operated cab sliding doors were provided with separate push button controls so that they could be operated by either the driver or the guard. In addition a pair of push buttons forward of the cab door on the outside of the car at platform level enabled the cab door to be closed or opened without a guard's position switch or driver's control switch being closed, but when either of these main switches was in use these push buttons became inoperative.

The door control arrangements — which have been standard equipment since the earlier days of air-operated doors — were provided, such as the external push buttons located on the end panels of the car body to enable platform staff to close the doors on that car under special control requirements; the outside door cocks which could be operated to open two door leaves in an emergency from the outside were also incorporated. Also provided were door indicator lights, which remained alight if any problem arose with the door interlock circuit, including of course any door failing to close.

Power for the door controls was provided by the motor alternator on the driving motor car on which the door controls had been cut in by the selection of the position switch. Motor alternators were installed on both motor cars of a three-car unit and they provided an ac supply of 115V. Each alternator supplied half the main fluorescent lighting in all three cars of

*Above:*
**A shunting control cabinet on the uncoupling non-driving motor car of 1973 Tube stock.** *LRT 76/2541*

the unit so that the failure of one motor alternator ensured at least that each car had half the lights. The motor alternators also drove fans on the same shaft which were used to cool the motoring and braking resistances. Transformer rectifier units were fed from the motor alternators, which converted the 115V ac to 50V dc to supply a control feed for traction, brake and door operation and for charging an emergency battery. While the motor alternators were running the batteries remained charged, but if they stopped, the batteries would feed the 50V dc circuit for a limited period.

Lighting on all cars was by 4ft fluorescent tubes, the emergency lights being fed directly from the batteries with converters to change the current back to ac again. Some of the car

advertisements were illuminated directly from the motor alternator, not through the lighting switches by a separate circuit. Twin headlights were provided — one on each side of the cab front — and were only illuminated when the cab was operative. Mounted on the headstock were twin electric tail lights which could be illuminated only when the cab operation had been closed down, but placed on the nearside headstock there was an additional tail light which could be used as a permanent stabling light, even when all other circuits had been switched off.

Heaters in all the passenger saloons and ventilation fans were also provided. These latter were fitted subsequently to the cars after delivery. This equipment was placed under the control of thermostats and the fans received their power from the batteries so that they would work for a time without the motor alternators running.

The main alterations to the internal features of the cars was an extra 9½in setting-back of the side screens inside the double doorways, and the provision of large vestibules at the cab ends. This extra space was provided specially to give some additional luggage space without obstructing the doorways. The low car height of tube stock makes it impossible to provide any form of luggage rack which would not be obstructive to standing passengers when not in use for luggage. This large stand-back at the double doorways — and in particular at the car ends — provided about 42sq ft of additional luggage space in each car compared with 1959 Tube stock, but the space could also be used by standing passengers.

The capacity of a 1973 Tube stock six-car train totalled 1,212 passengers of which 264 were provided with seats. This can be compared with the displaced seven-car 1959 Tube stock which had a total capacity of 1,158 passengers but with 24 more seated at 288. Each car of 1973 Tube stock actually seated 44, arranged in longi-tudinal seats at the car end bays with cross-seats in the middle bay of each car. The longitudinal seats were fitted with the split-level armrests, first fitted to the 1967 Tube stock.

The traction equipment, which was still of the basic PCM-type, was redesigned to provide rheostatic braking but using only a single camshaft. When rheostatic braking was first introduced on the 1967 Tube stock this was achieved by providing a second camshaft. The camshaft now controlled the starting resistance and the rheostatic braking resistors on both series and parallel steps for four LT118-type 300V traction motors which now run in series pairs. All four axles on a motor car were motored, controlled by one traction equipment, providing series-parallel connections when both pairs of motors finally became connected across the current supply. In order to reduce the size of the resistors for braking and enable full rheostatic braking to be accomplished under crush load conditions, these resistances were blown by fans provided on the motor alternators.

Load weighing was provided to give constant rates of acceleration and braking, whatever the train loading.

This arrangement replaced the mercury switch retardation control introduced originally with the 1938 Tube stock.

The braking control of the 1973 Tube stock was quite different from that previously fitted to London Transport trains, being based on the 'Westcode' system which employed coded electrical circuits to provide the control and safety features. The Westcode had two separate controlling circuits, one for normal service braking and the other an overriding circuit for emergency braking which incorporated all the safety features such as the passenger emergency alarms, tripcocks and dead person's handle. An entirely new type of passenger emergency alarm was incorporated, consisting of buttons instead of handles. The buttons could only be reset by the use of a Yale-type key.

The safety provision was based on a round-the-train electrical circuit which afforded the same security as that provided by the Westinghouse train pipe filled with compressed air. Any break in the circuit applied the emergency brake just as loss of air in the Westinghouse train pipe applied the emergency brake on earlier Underground trains.

The brake blocks were still applied to the wheels by air pressure from reservoirs carried on each car. Sufficient air pressure was retained in these reservoirs to provide at least two emergency brake applications, even if the main air supply had been lost.

The Westcode was a modern control system for an EP brake giving rapid and simultaneous operation on all cars. The brakes could be applied and released in seven equal steps of brake cylinder pressure, the brake force on each car being individually regulated by a load control system worked mechanically. Application of the brake was still under the control of the driver, but the coded application system as used on the 1973 Tube stock used only four of the seven possible steps.

On the 1973 Tube stock the Westcode system was used for service brake application combined with a rheostatic

brake. The motor cars had to attempt to reach the required retardation by the rheostatic braking, this only being supplemented by the air brake if the rheostatic brake did not meet the level of retardation required. The air brake first applied on the trailer car of each unit and then supplemented the rheostatic brake on the motor car. The air brake took over completely should the rheostatic brake fail to develop. The air brake cylinders were in fact the only items of brake equipment which were similar in design to the conventional braking equipment based on the Westinghouse air brake. The brake cylinder pressure was maintained against leakage at the appropriate pressure setting and could be said therefore to be self-lapping, maintaining the selected pressure until the position of the control valve was changed. The brake controller operated switches to make or

break three control train wires which worked on the three pilot magnet valves so that a specific sequence giving four steps of braking could be provided. In the 1973 Tube stock the pilot valves were energised to release the brakes and de-energised to apply, which made the system a fail-safe device.

A variable control valve was fitted to one bogie of each car. It was worked mechanically by the spring deflection, thus assessing the load on the car. The pressure emanating from this valve ensured that the brake pressure was adjusted to allow for increased car weight due to passenger load.

The bogies provided on 1973 Tube stock followed previous practice, having a wheelbase of 1.9m (6ft 3in) and a wheel diameter of 788mm (31in) when new. Both primary and secondary suspension was provided by chevron rubber. Weight reduction was achieved by providing the bogie headstock, the motor suspension tubes on the motor axle and the axle box yokes in aluminium. The axle box yokes were provided with an adjustment screw which enabled the bogie height to be altered when smaller wheels were fitted, since the minimum scrapping diameter of the wheels was 710mm.

An additional feature of the 1973 Tube stock was the use of wheelslide protection to reduce the incidence of flats. If the start of a wheel slow-up was detected, then a dump valve on the bogie was energised so that air in the brake cylinders associated with the wheels on the point of locking was released momentarily, allowing them to start rolling again when a re-application of the brakes occurred.

The most advanced piece of equipment installed on the 1973 Tube stock — originally called the 'Fault Annunciator', but later known as the Train Equipment Panel (TEP) — which provided the motorman with information about the equipment carried on the complete train. This panel not only informed the driver of the state of particular apparatus on the train but could be interrogated to determine the location of a malfunction. The indicator panel was placed on the offside console in the driving cab, providing a desk display of internally illuminated push buttons and indicators which provided the appropriate information. For example, in the case of the operation of a passenger emergency alarm applying the emergency brake automatically, the driver could interrogate the TEP to locate in which car the emergency button had been depressed.

The driving motor cars were fitted with hydraulically actuated handbrakes, the actuators normally being pressurised by means of a hydraulic intensifier from the compressed air supply. In an emergency however, the hydraulic power could be obtained by the use of a hand lever. If the motorman attempted to move the train with a

*Below left:*
**1973 Tube stock showing the aluminium axlebox yokes and bogie headstock.**
*LRT 75/3140*

*Below:*
**The standback arrangement at the double doorway position to provide space for luggage as specifically arranged for the Piccadilly Line service to Heathrow Airport.**
*LRT 76/2539*

*Above:*
**A 1973 tube stock three-car experimental train at Hainault alongside a service train of 1962 Tube stock. The 1973 Tube stock had been modified to take the Westinghouse Chopper Control System (CCS) for trial on the Hainault-Woodford automatic control section. The tripcock resetting cord has been brought up to the leading cab door.**
*Colin Marsden*

handbrake still 'on', a buzzer warning was given as well as a fault indication appearing on the TEP. By interrogating the panel an indication would be given which would show on which car the handbrake was still applied.

A six-car train was originally equipped with three compressors fitted to trailer cars: the trailer car placed in the west end 'A' units originally had two compressors, while those in the 'D' units had only one compressor fitted. It was found subsequently that air consumption was much less than expected so that the second compressor on the 'A' units was removed and used elsewhere. The double-ended units retained two compressors so that they could be used as a single train on the Aldwych shuttle service. The bulk of the compressors were of the conventional reciprocating design installed in previous tube stock, but a total of 46 of the hydrovane rotary type were provided for a large-scale trial of this type of machine.

The numbering system adopted for the 1973 Tube stock was also a break with tradition, as a reversion to simple three figure numbers was adopted, starting with 100 for the driving motor cars, even numbers being west end ('A') cars, and odd numbers east end ('D') cars. The double-ended unit motor cars, although numbered in the same series, had the '1' substituted by an '8', so that 253 was the last normal unit driving

motor car while 854 was the first double-ended unit motor car in the series. The uncoupling non-driving motor cars started with 300, with even numbers for 'A' end cars and odd for 'D' end cars, while trailer car numbering began at 500.

The first 1973 Tube stock entered regular service on the Piccadilly Line on 18 August 1975 because of delays in delivery of certain components. One train had entered service on 19 July 1975 to inaugurate the passenger route to Hatton Cross on the opening of the first extension of the line beyond Hounslow West. When introduced to the Piccadilly Line the first batch of 1973 Tube stock enabled the small number of 1938 Tube stock trains still working on the line to be withdrawn and later for seven-car trains of 1959 Tube stock to be transferred to the Northern Line.

Arrangements are now being made for the Piccadilly Line to be made suitable for OPO to become the first conventional tube line to be so operated. The 1973 Tube stock was designed with this type of operation in mind but

some modifications are required. An additional window wiper on the non-driving side of the cab is required and so is a new calling-on light, as the space occupied by the original fitting has been utilised for extra ventilation. It is also considered that additional door buttons should be available while looking forward, so these have to be fitted on the driving consoles.

A Royal opening of the Piccadilly Line extension to Terminal 4 at Heathrow Airport took place on 1 April 1986, but the actual passenger service did not begin until 12 April. This new extension was in the form of a loop, so the westbound trains work through Terminal 4 into Heathrow Central, the original terminal, but do not call at Terminal 4 in the eastbound direction. This means that the 1973 Tube stock trains now turn each time they run into Heathrow, introducing the problem of wrong way trains to the Piccadilly Line. To assist in overcoming the disadvantages arising, end identification stickers have been placed on both the driving and uncoupling non-driving motor cars, indicating 'A' or 'D' ends.

# 22.  1983 Tube Stock

Plans for the Fleet Line originated as far back as 1946 when proposals for such a line were included in the *Railway (London) Plan* published in that year. More detailed proposals involved a line from Baker Street to Lewisham in three stages: Stage I from Baker Street to Charing Cross connected with the existing Bakerloo Line at Baker Street but took over the Stanmore and Wembley Park branch to make up the Fleet Line, restoring the Bakerloo Line to its original form. Stage II was intended to extend the line from Charing Cross to Fenchurch Street; while Stage III continued the line on to Lewisham or Docklands, taking in part of the East London Line on the way. In the event, only Stage I was completed by which time it was renamed the Jubilee Line. It is now unlikely that any further sections will be completed for several years.

The rolling stock requirement was helped by the delay in authorising any construction beyond Stage I, enabling 1972 Mk II stock to be purchased to fulfil three distinct roles: to enable some 1938 Tube stock to be scrapped earlier than originally planned; to

provide the initial service on the Jubilee Line; and finally to replace the reconstructed 1938 Tube stock on the Bakerloo Line after a completely new design of rolling stock had been obtained for the Jubilee Line. The 1938 Tube stock rehabilitation programme was finally approved to improve the Bakerloo Line service after the opening of the Jubilee Line until the 1972 Mk II stock could be released to take over the service on the delivery of new stock for the Jubilee Line.

This arrangement bought time for the development of ATO and OMO systems for eventual use on the Jubilee Line. However, technical, economic and staffing problems further delayed such provisions and there has since been a change in the future proposals. The development aims have been concentrated not only on automatic working but on driverless trains, and the emphasis of this change is now central to the future of the Central Line. At this

time it had been envisaged that the 1938 Tube stock would begin to be replaced in 1982 when they were becoming a maintenance liability.

In June 1982 London Transport placed a firm order for 15 trains of what became named 1983 Tube stock, comprising 30 three-car units all of the double-cab type, and there was an option for a further 15 trains so that the whole of the Jubilee Line might be equipped with this stock subsequently. The order was placed with Metro-Cammell of Birmingham at a cost of over £1 million for each three-car unit. It had been intended that 30 trains would be ordered for the Jubilee Line, but a combination of service reduction — such as cutting back the Bakerloo service to Queens Park from September 1982 — and the reduction in maintenance requirements over all the tube lines meant it was possible to make 15 trains of 1972 Tube stock Mk II available for the Jubilee Line service in

*Below:*
**A 1983 Tube stock train in Charing Cross station.** *LRT 24013-2*

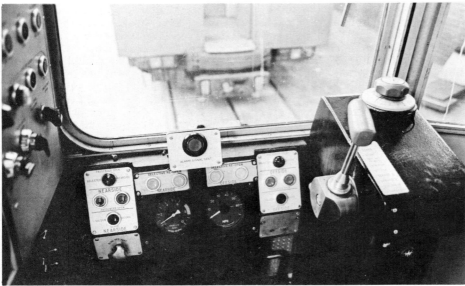

*Top:*
**A 1983 Tube stock train under test between Acton Town and Northfields.** *Brian Hardy*

*Above:*
**The 1983 tube stock driver's control position after conversion for one-person operation. On the right is the 'joystick' control handle which regulates braking as well as driving. The array of operating buttons are clearly marked.** *R. Greenaway*

addition to the 15 new trains of 1983 Tube stock.

As initially proposed, and abiding by the principle that each tube line should be equipped with one type of stock only wherever possible, the Jubilee Line was to be equipped with 30 1983 Tube stock trains, with further similar trains to be ordered if the line was ever extended beyond Charing Cross (the initial terminus of the line), and the Bakerloo Line with 33 trains of 1972 Tube stock Mk II. This arrangement was superseded by the introduction of politically motivated economy measures, so that the proposed order for 1983 Tube stock was curtailed to 15 trains only.

Arriving on 27 August 1983 behind a BR Class 25 diesel locomotive, the first unit of 1983 Tube stock was delivered directly to Neasden depot and not to Ruislip depot where previous deliveries of new stock had been received from car builders since about 1950. Another numbering system was adopted for this stock, west end driving motors starting at 3601 and the east end motors from 3701, while the trailer cars were numbered from 4601.

The three-car units were made up from two driving motor cars with a trailer between. Each car seated 40 passengers in longitudinal seats and eight in transverse seats at the centre of the car. The trailer cars had a standing capacity of a further 161, but the driving motor cars with the space required for the cab had a standing capacity somewhat less at 139. In addition, the trailer cars were slightly shorter over body ends, being 57.95ft (17,676mm) long, while the motor cars were 58.11ft (17,726mm). The official dimensions of vehicles were now given completely in metric. A six-car train of 1983 Tube stock had a carrying capacity of 1,262 passengers with 288 seated.

In many respects the 1983 Tube stock was a tube-train version of the success-

ful surface line 'D' stock introduced to the District Line, delivery of which was only completed in 1983. The 1983 Tube stock was the first tube-type train to have passenger open door control with single leaf doors as introduced on the 'D' stock, but not the first type of tube train to carry the guard in the driver's cab.

Other items common with the 'D' stock included the provision of a driver's seat which was adjustable in three directions — forwards and backwards, up and down and swivelling. Two window wipers were fitted to the main front cab windows for the benefit of any second man carried in the cab. In addition, the driving motor cars were provided with headlights, tail lights and stabling lights, as well as a calling-on light in preparation for eventual conversion to OMO when this is arranged for tube train operation in single-bore tunnels without the Victoria Line type of ATO.

The trains had flat cab fronts without the wrap-round windows which had been fitted to all new tube stock following the 1967 Tube stock. The introduction of a flat appearance was due to the fitting of shatter-proof glass, difficult to produce in curved form.

The driver's cab arrangements have been much improved over previous stocks. The Train Equipment Panel (TEP) fitted to 1973 Tube stock has been replaced by the Programmable Logic System (PLS) which gives illuminated indicators only when a defect occurs.

The destination blind was motor driven by push button operation, but the train set numbers were set up by thumb switches. The security lock fitted to 'J' door entrance to the cab for the passenger saloon was a new type designed for the purpose, being much less obtrusive than those previously added to existing doors when this feature was required to prevent easy access to driving cabs. The now standard communication systems were provided, including cab-to-cab telephones, public address and a train radio giving two-way contact with the line control office.

The passenger emergency arrangement was provided by push buttons similar to those on the 1973 Tube stock. When any one of these buttons was operated, an illuminated indication was provided in the car itself above the car number plate, but in addition the car concerned was displayed on the PLS unit in the driving cab. The buttons on the car can only be reset by the insertion of the operator's key.

As it was not intended to operate any of the three-car units singly as trains, only one compressor per unit mounted on the trailer was provided, although arrangements can be made to fit a second compressor if necessary.

Three Maudslay motor alternators were also fitted to each trailer car, two to provide the lighting circuits at 850

hertz, 115V ac each, one providing half the lighting on all three cars of the unit, the other motor alternator at 50 hertz, 240V ac, the power for the ceiling-mounted fans.

The electrical equipment for the units was provided by Brush of Loughborough, its supply being the first real breakaway from the PCM-type of control which had been fitted to all tube trains since the 1938 Tube stock.

The bogies were built by BREL (British Railways Engineering Ltd) at Derby, and although a Westinghouse braking system was used, Knorr Bremse brake cylinders were fitted to the trucks. The driving motor cars were fitted with sleet brushes and five trailers with de-icing dispensing equipment. All this equipment could be controlled from any leading driving cab.

The end single doors of the car bodies had an opening of 2ft 3in (685.8mm) the accepted standard for such doors on

*Above:*
**The interior of 1983 Tube stock: note the roof fans and lighting illuminators.** *LRT 23292*

*Below:*
**Preparation for service of two units of 1983 Tube stock in Neasden depot. Note the change in style of the top ventilator grilles.** *Brian Hardy*

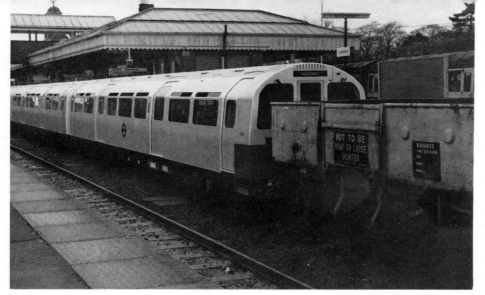

previous stocks, but instead of pairs of double doors on the rest of the body sides, single doors 3ft 6in (1,067mm) were provided. Another radical change was that the pressure settings applied to these doors were different. The air pressure settings on the smaller doors was 2.2 bars (31.9lb/sq in) while on the larger doors it was set higher at 3.3 bars (47.9lb/sq in). The control arrangement allowed for passenger-open guard-close as the normal mode. The passenger control buttons followed the style already established on the 'D' stock on the District Line, with switching provided to allow for the guard to completely control the door operations if necessary.

The ventilation was of an improved pattern incorporating seven extractor fans located in the ceilings, together with inflow ducts placed over the side windows. In addition, the fluorescent tubes were provided with covers for the first time in tube stock. These luminator fittings provided back-lighting for the transparent commercial adverts as well as the saloon lighting with glare. Car heating was arranged to be thermostatically controlled.

The bogies were designed as box frames without headstocks.

The first 1983 Tube stock went into service 1 May 1984 and triggered off another general transfer of tube rolling stock between lines. Each 1983 Tube stock train entering service released a 1972 Tube stock Mk II train for transfer to the Northern Line, which in turn released a 1959 Tube stock to go from the Northern Line to the Bakerloo Line, allowing a 1938 Tube stock train to be withdrawn.

With the need to restore the service cuts introduced in 1982 and to provide an improved service on all the tube lines in the near future, 16½ more trains — that is 33 units — of 1983 Tube stock type were ordered in 1986. In this way the original plan formulated some 10 years before will be fulfilled.

All the trains on the Jubilee Line are to be provided with one group of stock suitable for one-person operation. Upon completion of delivery of the additional cars the 1983 Tube stock designed with OPO in mind will enable not only this to be achieved on the Jubilee Line but on the Bakerloo Line as well, by the transfer of the fleet of 1972 Mk II Tube stock to this line. This fleet was also constructed with OPO in mind. These, together with the consequential transfers of rolling stock, will leave only the Northern Line with mixed stock until the next round of rolling stock requirements.

*Top:*
**1983 tube stock being delivered to Neasden depot between match wagons.**
*Brian Hardy*

*Below:*
**1983 Tube stock alongside a 1959 Tube stock train at Queens Park depot during running-in trials.** *Brian Hardy*

# 23.  1986 Tube Stock

The development of London Transport tube rolling stock since the 1938 Tube stock design has been evolutionary rather than revolutionary, although one or two major changes have been made with, for example, automatic train operation (ATO) and rheostatic braking on the 1967 Tube stock, and with longer cars and a modern brake control system on the 1973 Tube stock. The principal components, the car bodies and the traction control equipment, have in fact changed very little in comparison with designs elsewhere in the world. This has been partly due to the need to provide compatibility with existing rolling stock and maintenance requirements and partly because the design has met the reliability standards required. Although five different designs have been produced in the last 16 years, none have introduced any major changes.

The new rolling stock programmes of 1959/62 caught up the backlog following the postwar restrictions on capital expenditure and subsequent stocks only provided the immediate needs without any development period being available. Arising out of the fact that tube rolling stock normally has a life of 35 years and that there has been little expansion of the system needing an increase of the fleet size, rolling stock replacement will not be required to begin before 1994, when some 1,600 cars will need replacement over a period of some six years. It was however thought desirable to spread this replacement over some 10 years as the capacity of the car building industry had now been reduced and begin this work in about 1990. At the same time the signalling on the Central Line would also require renewal, enabling an automatic train operation system to be developed in parallel with the rolling stock renewal programme.

Therefore, in May 1984 it was announced that three four-car prototype tube trains would be ordered to test a number of new design features in preparation for the ordering of new stock for the Central Line, and also to obtain comparisons between available manufacturers' rolling stock and equipment. It was also felt to be desirable at the same time to update the appearance of tube trains within the restrictions of the tunnel size.

With the Hainault Loop in mind, reversible coupling was included in the specification so that each of the three prototypes consists of two two-car units having a driving cab at one end of one car only, with the two cars semi-permanently coupled together, and two of the two-car units forming a four-car train. The automatic coupling arrangements between units and the controls of all three trains are compatible so that any combination of two-car units can be made up into an eight-car train for operation in passenger service after the test trials are completed.

When the original R49 all-aluminium surface stock cars were scrapped recently, the body structures were in almost perfect condition. Tube cars, although sheathed in aluminium, have continued with steel body structures because equivalent stiffness in aluminium would require deep members impeding access to equipment unless some radical alteration in design was made. The use of wide extrusions welded together offered a solution if the whole body side could be load-bearing, thus providing a lighter structure reducing energy consumption.

Using this type of construction, the car lengths are 52.49ft (16m) and 51.18ft (15.6m), the longer car being the one with the driving cab. In addition, this

*Below:*
**The interior of a Style B BREL train at the driving cab end. The new type of cab door access handle is clearly visible.** *BREL*

construction enables externally-mounted sliding doors without door pockets to be provided, including overhead positioned linear door operators. The doors themselves include door-opening buttons mounted on the doors. Provided also is a door-closing button for use mainly at terminal stations in order to avoid the trains

standing with doors open during the whole of the layover period. In addition, audible tones for opening and closing to warn the passengers are provided.

To compare changes which were possible in the restricted space of a tube car because the construction

enabled a flat floor to be provided — even on motor cars — three different interior layouts and colour schemes are incorporated. These different internal layouts have been provided to test passenger access and circulation arrangements. There are double doorways and single doorways at the car

*Bottom:*
**An interior view of the Style C 1986 Tube stock prototype train, at the car builder's works.** *Metro-Cammell*

*Left:*
**An exterior view of the Style C 1986 Tube stock outside the car builder's works at Birmingham.**

body ends. The number of seats vary between 32 and 42 depending on the layout, and one design includes perch seats beside each doorway.

In the late 1960s, power semiconductors became reliable components, making possible the development of 'solid state'-type control of the traction motor's current. Trials were made with dc 'chopper' controls on the Hainault-Woodford section, but these equipments proved to be unreliable, the energy savings following the eliminations of losses through the starting resistances were found not to be significant, and finally the risk of pulsed currents interfering with signalling circuits caused the experiments to be terminated. Later developments have shown that such equipments are now more reliable, can be made compatible with signalling systems and can provide regeneration, making the economics much more attractive. However, to achieve results with this type of equipment all axles must be motored, so a four-car prototype train has 16 traction motors.

Three different makes of 'chopper' equipment are being fitted from three different manufacturers, GEC, Brush and Brown-Boveri. The thyristor control provides both rheostatic and regenerative braking, but friction brakes are also provided on the wheel treads on two of the trains and on discs on the other.

On two of the trains, conventional bogies with welded steel box constructions are provided with rubber chevrons for the primary suspension and air bags with an anti-roll bar for the secondary suspension. One of these trains is provided with bogies built by Duewag of Germany and the other with bogies by Hunslet of Leeds. These two trains are being constructed by Metro-Cammell of Birmingham. They are provided with lightweight fully-sprung traction motors with flexible drive to axle-mounted gearboxes.

The new car body construction makes it possible to minimise penetration of the floor by bogie components, although small recesses are still necessary to provide clearance for the 700mm diameter wheels, even though they have been reduced to some 90mm less than the previous standard for tube trains.

An independent project for trials of a steerable bogie designed by BREL and a more conventional 'H' frame bogie were made early in 1986 and fitted to cars 3305 and 3230 of 1972 Tube stock working on the Northern Line. The third train being constructed by BREL, the train fitted with Brush electrical equipment, has also been fitted with steerable bogies. The steerable bogies are provided with axle-hung motors and with resilient wheels. The latter have for many years found favour with modern tramway systems both on the European continent and in America, but could not be used on tube trains because the brake blocks generally worked on the wheel treads. Resilient wheels, however, can be used in conjunction with disc brakes which are installed on the steerable bogies.

It has always been a problem to provide adequate ventilation in a tube train, both while moving and when stationary, without creating draughts or excessive noise, so the prototype trains are being used to experiment again with such equipment.

It is also intended to provide station indicators in each car to announce the name of the next station. Of the dot-matrix type, these will be controlled by a micro-processor which may subsequently be triggered from the track. The train destination indicators will also be of the dot-matrix type. All modern communication systems are installed and the heating is controlled by thermostats.

The braking systems will be shared between Westinghouse and Davies & Metcalfe, while some of the units will be fitted with hydrovane compressors.

The numbering of the cars has reverted to a very simple system: the driving motor cars have been numbered 11 to 16 and the non-driving motor cars 21 to 26, the compatible pairs sharing the common digit. The trains will operate in passenger service on the Jubilee Line, working from Neasden depot when the initial testing period has been completed.

*Below:*
**An exterior view of the Style B 1986 Tube stock at the British Rail Engineering Ltd works at Derby.** *BREL*

# Appendix

## Dimensions of Tube Stock Driving Motor Cars

| Type of stock | Overall length (ft in) | (metres) | Overall width (ft in) | (metres) | Weight (tons) | Number of motors | Number of seats | Notes |
|---|---|---|---|---|---|---|---|---|
| 1903 Central London | 45   6 | 13.87 | 8   6 | 2.59 | 23.0 | 2 | 42 | 1 |
| 1906/07 Gate stock | 50   3 | 15.32 | 8   9 | 2.67 | 27.5 | 2 | 36 | 2 |
| 1923 Standard stock | 51   4 | 15.65 | 8   6 | 2.59 | 32.0 | 2 | 30 | 3 |
| 1927 Standard stock | 51   4 | 15.65 | 8   6 | 2.59 | 29.0 | 2 | 30 | 3 |
| 1931 Standard stock | 51   5 | 15.67 | 8   3 | 2.51 | 31.8 | 2 | 30 | 3 |
| 1938 Tube stock | 52   4 | 15.95 | 8   6 | 2.59 | 27.4 | 2 | 42 | 4 |
| 1959/62 Tube stock | 52   3 | 15.93 | 8   6 | 2.59 | 26.6 | 2 | 42 | 4/5 |
| 1960 Tube stock | 52   0 | 15 85 | 8   6 | 2.59 | 30.1 | 4 | 40 | 6 |
| 1967 Tube stock | 52   9 | 16.08 | 8   8 | 2.64 | 28.6 | 4 | 40 | 7 |
| 1972 Tube stock | 52   9 | 16.08 | 8   8 | 2.64 | 28.6 | 4 | 40 | 8 |
| 1973 Tube stock | 57   4 | 17.47 | 8   7 | 2.63 | 27.2 | 4 | 44 | 9 |
| 1983 Tube stock | 58   2 | 17.73 | 8   7 | 2.63 | 25.7 | 4 | 48 | 9 |

1. Usually operated in six-car trains with two motor cars.
2. Usually operated in five- and six-car trains with two motor cars.
3. Operated in six-car trains with two motor cars; six- and seven-car trains with three motor cars; and eight-car trains with four motor cars.
4. Operated in seven-car trains with five motor cars.
5. Operated in eight-car trains with six motor cars.
6. Regular operation in four-car units with two motor cars.
7. Operated in eight-car trains with four motor cars.
8. Operated in seven-car trains with four motor cars.
9. Operated in six-car trains with four motor cars.

## 1938 Tube Stock Fleet

|  | Driving motors | Non-driving motors | Uncoupling Non-driving motors | Trailers |
|---|---|---|---|---|
| 1938 Metropolitan-Cammell | 644 | 107 | — | — |
| 1938 Birmingham | — | 99 | — | 271 |
| 1927 Converted Acton Works | — | — | — | 58 |
| 1949 Birmingham | — | — | 70 | 21 |
| 1935 Converted Acton Works | — | — | — | 18 |
| 1938 Converted Acton Works | — | −22 | +22 | — |
| *Total* | **644** | **184** | **92** | **368** |

## Standard Tube Stock

|  | Bakerloo | | | *Stock allocation 1935*<br>Piccadilly | | | Northern | | |
|---|---|---|---|---|---|---|---|---|---|
|  | M | T | CT | M | T | CT | M | T | CT |
| 1923 stock | — | — | — | — | — | — | 81 | 45 | 36 |
| 1924 stock | — | — | — | — | — | — | 52 | 50 | 25 |
| 1925 stock | — | — | — | — | — | — | 48 | 5 | 67 |
| 1926 stock | — | — | — | — | — | — | 64 | 48 | — |
| 1927 Metro stock | 30 | 25 | 15 | — | 40 | 6 | 80 | 95 | 15 |
| 1927 Feltham stock | 29 | 15 | 18 | 37 | 22 | 48 | 11 | — | 2 |
| 1929 Feltham stock | 1 | 2 | 1 | 17 | 15 | 17 | — | — | — |
| 1930 Metro stock | 22 | 20 | 20 | — | — | — | — | — | — |
| 1930 Feltham stock | — | — | — | 2 | 4 | — | — | — | — |
| 1931 stock | — | — | — | 145 | 130 | — | — | — | — |
| 1934 stock | — | — | — | 26 | — | — | — | — | — |
| 1920 Cammell Laird | — | 20 | 20 | — | — | — | — | — | — |
| *Total* | **82** | **82** | **74** | **227** | **211** | **71** | **336** | **243** | **145** |

## Standard Tube Stock As Built

| Builder's date | Builder | Motors | Number of cars<br>Trailers | Control trailers |
|---|---|---|---|---|
| 1923 exp stock | Gloucester Railway Car & Wagon Co | — | 1 | 1 |
| 1923 exp stock | Leeds Forge | — | 1 | — |
| 1923 exp stock | Metropolitan Carriage Wagon & Finance Co | — | 1 | — |
| 1923 exp stock | Birmingham Railway Car & Wagon Co | — | 1 | — |
| 1923 exp stock | Cammell Laird & Co Ltd | — | 1 | — |
| 1923 stock | Cammell Laird | 41 | 40 | — |
| 1923 stock | Metropolitan | 40 | — | 35 |
| 1923 stock | Birmingham | — | 35 | — |
| 1924 stock | Cammell Laird | — | — | 25 |
| 1924 stock | Metropolitan | 52 | — | — |
| 1924 stock | Birmingham | — | 50 | — |
| 1925 stock | Cammell Laird | 48 | — | — |
| 1925 stock | Metropolitan | — | 5 | 67 |
| 1926 stock | Metropolitan | 64 | 48 | — |
| 1927 stock | Metropolitan | 110 | 160 | 36 |
| 1927 stock | Feltham | 77 | 37 | 68 |
| 1929 stock | Feltham | 18 | 17 | 18 |
| 1930 stock | Metropolitan-Cammell | 22 | 20 | 20 |
| 1930 stock | Feltham | 2 | 4 | — |
| 1931 stock | Metropolitan-Cammell | 145 | — | — |
| 1931 stock | Birmingham | — | 90 | — |
| 1931 stock | Gloucester | — | 40 | — |
| 1934 stock | Metropolitan-Cammell | 26 | — | — |
| *Grand total* | | **645** | **551** | **270** |

*Left:*
**The first 1938 Tube stock train as delivered at Golders Green depot in 1938 in seven-car formation and without destination boards.** *LRT U27428*

*Below:*
**A head-on view of 1973 Tube stock as built with original position of the calling on light above the driver; tail lights and stabling light are on the headstock. Tripcock resetting cord and isolating cocks for couplers and tripcock are plainly visible. The 'D' rings on the headstock are provided to enable rail chains to be fitted in an emergency to prevent an immobile unit from running away on an incline.**
*LRT 3006/4/11*